Bernard Buffet

Mᵉ Blot
incertain

A CERTAIN MONSIEUR BLOT

•

PIERRE DANINOS

Translated from the French by Robin Chancellor

•

Illustrated by
BERNARD BUFFET

•

NEW YORK • SIMON AND SCHUSTER • 1962

Any resemblance of persons living or dead to the characters in this book is purely coincidental. With the exception, of course, of the similarity of Monsieur Paul Stanislas Blot—actuary, forty-five years old, married, two children—to himself.

CONTENTS

1

TRANSPARENCY

ANOTHER CONTEST. A "Great" one, naturally, since in
this great country of ours no newspaper or television company would dream of sponsoring any contest without
qualifying it as Great. And the questions it asks! "*Who*

11

are you?" If I simply reply, "Blot, Paul, actuary,* age
forty-five, married, two children," will this satisfy them?
Possibly. Not me.

To begin with, my name alone, albeit only one syllable,
demands more than one line. There is so much one could
say about it. As a word, it gets blurted rather than pronounced. Four letters that plop out and instantly vanish, a
wan little light puffed out by the wind, barely included in
the Larousse, in the shape of a common noun: "BLOT
. . . a job lot of merchandise."

No doubt there are powerful and venerable Blots, brilliant Blots, Grand Officer of the Legion of Honor Blots,
Company President Blots, Director-General Blots, cap-
tains of industry—in short, Blots who have made their
name. They should not bear me any ill will. With humble
apologies to all the Blots in the world, those in the Social
Register and those in the housing developments, those in
the provinces and those in the Jockey Club, I have to admit that the transitory, tepid, ephemeral qualities of this
name which slips so lightly off the tongue have long
haunted me and haunt me still.

If Bonaparte had been born with such a name, he would
never have founded an empire. One cannot conquer
Prussia, one doesn't overrun Europe, with a name like
Blot. France may be divided into Bonapartists and anti-
Bonapartists, Gaullists and anti-Gaullists, but how could
one possibly conceive of Blotists and anti-Blotists? With-

---

* A *specialist in matters of general statistics (death rate, accidents, etc.)
and financial arithmetic, with particular reference to life insurance.*

out even going so far as Napoleon or Vercingetorix, their crushing syllables fraught with glory and doom, I cherish an envy of simple names like Buffet, La Fontaine, Chevalier or Lamoureux, which force their way into the public consciousness until their original meaning is forgotten and they become synonymous with those who bear them. On closer examination, what a falling off there is in names! The telephone is probably the best barometer of immortality. For the few patronymics which survive the manhandling of the Ministry of Posts, Telephone and Telegraph and fulfill their function in the dialing system without suffering any loss thereby—RICHelieu, VOLtaire, BALzac— just think of all the MOLitors, LECourbes, TRUdaines and other BOTzaris who are nothing more today (except to friends of the family) than a telephone exchange reduced to three letters!

Can my face have been influenced by this name? I sometimes wonder, when I see people's eyes skid off it to focus elsewhere. No ridges, no planes to hold their gaze. I am made of that anonymous putty whose shapeless features are entered in passports as "average." Forehead: average. Mouth: average. Distinguishing characteristics: nil. I have been told that when I was a baby I had blue eyes. So has everyone. Some keep them. Mine turned gray. Like the rest of me. I have the feeling of having dissolved into grayness. And of going through life, not as flesh and bone, but like a radiophotograph, a compound of dots and dashes the same as certain figures in advertisements whose

13

faces, built up solely out of crosshatchings or groups of dots, could be anybody's and are nobody's.

How many times during lunches or dinners have I had the impression of being a grille through which the neighbors on each side of me converse? If by chance they stop using me as a transmission screen, mysterious forces, after making them momentarily oscillate to left and right, impel them toward their nearest fellow guests—never toward me. It's as if I didn't exist, or simply that I make no impression on people's retinas.

I no longer feel astonished that the mere act of my appearing in the doorway of a shop should impel the one and only available salesgirl to telephone to her best friend or withdraw into the back premises. Just as, in a restaurant, I have long since grown accustomed to seeing the waiter flee to the kitchens as soon as I signal him. Can it be hunger that makes me so gossamer-thin that I am mistaken by the staff for an empty seat? Possibly, but even if I have eaten I become hardly any more substantial in the eyes of certain persons, notably the young ladies in the post office. I have only to show my nose at the counter for the clerk to go off, clutching a pile of forms, to the chief postmaster, with whom she launches into a long confabulation. Why? And why, if I hold out my coat to the checkroom attendant, is my arm always the last one she chooses out of ten similar arms?*

---

* *The most infuriating thing is that this faculty of transparency ceases the moment it could be of any use to me. Invisible to the eyes of officials, taxi drivers and shop assistants (I am whenever I need them, but they swarm*

Are there other beings in the world who suffer from transparency like me and for whom the doctors ought to prescribe opacity cures? I hope so. It makes things so much easier to bear if you know there are others as little favored as yourself! Should these lines ever see the light of day, I'd like them to be dedicated to all those who go through life in filigree, to those who could sit for thirty years under an apple tree without a law of universal gravitation ever entering their heads, to all the unobtrusive of the world who, on reaching sixty-five, after having received the best medical attention from good doctors, depart on tiptoe.

The phenomenon of transparency of which I am speaking first made its appearance when I was at school. Hardly a month goes by without bringing us a new biography of some famous man. Whatever the origins of this fame, the opening lines of these works are always identical: the hero is invariably marked by a precocious genius. Was he a (great) surgeon? "From early childhood, he showed such an appetite for dissection that he spent every spare mo-

---

as soon as I don't), I become phosphorescent to the eyes of people I would like to avoid, whether it's the young man selling a students' magazine, who buttonholes me in the street and starts giving me complexes ("I hope this doesn't mean you're against youth, monsieur!"), or the drunk in the last train home, a living roulette ball declaiming, "Li—ber—ty, E—qual—ity, Fra—ter—nity," and veering from one traveler to another until he finally fastens on the number of his choice: however much I avoid catching his eye, I am always that number. And in summer in the casinos, however small I make myself look in my seat while the magician hunts in vain for a volunteer to share in his experiment, I'm almost certain he'll end by making me go up on the stage so that he can extract an egg from my nose.

ment opening up the bodies of insects and reptiles." A (great) general? "From early youth, the science of military strategy absorbed him so deeply that every evening he reenacted one of the great battles of history with the help of lead soldiers and paper flags."

Well, as for me, from my earliest infancy at school I was marked by absolutely nothing. Unlike so many famous men, I wasn't even an *enfant terrible*, the ringleader of a gang, who the teachers swore would never come to anything whatsoever. No. My teachers said no such thing to me. No more did they tell me I would come to something. In fact, I never had very good reports. Nor very bad ones either. Halfway between the leaders and the laggards, I occupied that neutral, mediocre and pallid zone—grayness already—that no man's land of those dedicated to averageness, to whom teachers are utterly indifferent. Just as the newspapers are interested only in film stars and criminals, so teachers display any passion, whether tender or violent, only toward the aces and the dunces.

Even physically I never claimed their attention. Time and again, especially in history class, would I see M. Nizard take the whole lesson for two or three pupils. The whole class could listen, but he was describing the meeting on the Field of the Cloth of Gold or the Sicilian Vespers solely, it seemed, for Delpic, Gourovitch or Klotz. For one long hour he never took his eyes off one of these three faces, to the exclusion of all the others. Like some other comrades of mine who were equally ignored, I often tried to attract M. Nizard's attention by some gesture, folding or unfold-

16

ing my arms, or sometimes with a pocket mirror, but his eyes would skip over me as if I had been reported absent and, after roving around the class as if in a dream, would once more seek out Klotz, Gourovitch or Delpic as their focal point. I simply didn't interest him.

M. Nizard wasn't the only one. Certain instructors, quick enough to single out their whipping boy or their pet, sometimes went for several weeks without even giving my face a name. In the last year, M. Chabal noticed at the end of the first semester that he had never asked me a question. Whenever he designated one of those who were snapping their fingers to answer a question—"You!"—his outstretched finger aimed to my right or left, never at me. One December afternoon, as he was looking down the list of names entered in his notebook, he realized that he had forgotten all about me.

"You there! What's your name again?"

"Blot, m'sieur."

"Well," he said, "it *should* be an easy name to remember."

Probably too easy. He had swallowed it.

"Sticks to the middle of the class. Could stick out more." Such were the remarks, tainted with that second-rate wit teachers find it hard to resist, that my instructors wrote on my end-of-term reports.

In life it has gone on just the same. My subscription to averageness has never been canceled. Everything about me is average: my figure, my brains, my rent, my class. At first sight, then, I might believe myself made to order for this contest. And yet, if I enter it, it will be without conviction. Why shouldn't I admit it? I've never had any luck where chance is concerned. I've never been one of those who win lotteries, no raffle ever brought any prize my way, I never find myself among the 38,750 people questioned by the Institute of Public Opinion on the international situation. I often study the newspaper photographs of those total strangers interrogated by reporters who christen them "the man in the street," to find out what they think of the government, the cost of living, television or the women's vote. Picked at random from the masses, they represent what I am, they say things I might have said, they are me. But I'm never one of them.

But what exactly does entering the contest entail? More, of course, than simply drawing up a list of the ten principal good points and the ten principal shortcomings of the French. (Why ten? Doubtless because neither nine nor eleven is a boundary figure, one of those round figures which betoken something serious. Atlases list the ten biggest cities in the world, tennis experts the ten best players in the world. Five, ten, fifteen, twenty—yes. Four, eight, eleven, sixteen—no. Odd!) You must also, by giving your own vital statistics, your traits of character, your way of life and your average expenditures, make fate and figures the judges of whether you yourself are the Average Frenchman.

I have often wondered whether there exists somewhere in France, like the standard measure of a meter in the

Pavillon de Sèvres, a prototype citizen combining all the characteristics of what is customarily called the Average Frenchman. Or whether this ideal Dupont to whom people so endlessly refer, measuring his capacity for wine with as much mathematical precision as his faith in democracy, is a purely mythical creation dressed up in a panoply of statistics and inflated with opinions by the popular press.

I would be very surprised if this competition provided the answer. All the same, even if I haven't, like so vast a number of my fellow citizens, developed a mania for contests and an aptitude for coming up with the date of the next-to-last performance of Moliere's *Le Malade imaginaire* and the name of George Sand's third poodle under the floodlights of the television studio, I love a gamble; I have always had a taste for figures and statistics; my position as an actuary employed by an insurance company has accustomed me for years to calculating probabilities and working out graphs. Why not, for once, put my capabilities to the test for a more frivolous cause than that of longevity? I won't say no.

Yet I see here another opportunity: The very nature of the questions, often personal, regarding character, conjugal life, the children, prompts me to take stock of myself and also to examine those around me. Can it be the approach of fifty which urges me to write, as so many others have done, out of a need to confess and a desire to "leave something behind"? I don't think so. Figures and statistics, those two teats that nurture all actuaries, hardly predispose one to prose; and in the event that I do carry this project through, any reader will very quickly discover my inborn need for classification and co-ordinates. Now, even if I am quite prepared to demonstrate that love obeys laws as strict as the unknown quantities of second-degree equations, I have to recognize that analysis of the passions is ill suited to graphic tables and abscissas. To tell the truth, I simply feel a desire, since vacation time has come, to take advantage of the respite to collect my thoughts and, by means of this questionnaire, take my bearings in this world into which I have been brought to live. That is the origin of these notes, written at random and in the margin, as it were, of the more concise replies demanded by the contest.

2

THE DAILY ROUND

1. What role does your occupation play in your life?
2. Do you like your work?
3. Are you satisfied with your relations with your boss?
4. Do you come into contact with him frequently, intermittently, not at all?
5. Are you content with your lot?
6. . . .

CONTENT WITH my lot?

A Frenchman does not consider himself fully rewarded in civilian life unless he is a general. In my firm the title "general" and wall-to-wall carpeting—distinctive emblems of the highest echelon, the summit of the hierarchical pyramid—are the symbols of omnipotence. Thus we have a president-director general, two directors general, one co-director general, four assistant directors general, one secretary general, two assistant secretaries general, and so on.

General is a magic word; there can be no mistaking the instant effect it produces when coupled with the humble

21

rank of secretary. It's wonderful to see how it inflates this inferior denomination, how it makes it glitter with the light of its invisible stars. *General* embodies power, brilliance, the notion of leadership, of superiority. It presupposes over-all control, breadth of scope, and confers on everything which follows or precedes it a character of gravity: general instructions, general notes on administration, general management, general conference on management (not to be confused with conference on general management, which takes place higher up).

For my part, I have little contact with the president–director general. I don't complain. In a general way (if I dare qualify the way thus), I never have any luck with top people. I realize this anew every time the demands of my job bring me into consultation with one of these business chiefs in order to revise or set up a pension or life insurance plan. When I telephone them, they are "in conference" or engaged with someone, and when they do receive me they never stop telephoning. I believe the best thing to do, if you want to be sure of getting them, is to phone them from Passy or Auteuil and make the operator announce the call as coming from Buenos Aires or New York. Even during the most important meeting, they find it hard to resist snatching up the receiver when the secretary's voice says, "Mexico on line one" or "New York holding on line two." When you're lucky enough to have New York like that (wouldn't you almost say the skyscrapers were bowing?) you don't let such an opportunity slip by.

I've had the good fortune, during what is already a long

career, to be the privileged witness of numerous conversations of this kind, at a thousand or fifteen hundred francs a minute. What has always struck me is the vital importance of the dialogue: "How is Betty? . . . And the youngster? . . . Seen anything of the So-and-Sos? . . . I'm coming over to see you, but not before October." (A top man is always on the point of going to New York, if not of coming back from it.) "By the way, since Philippe is going over next week, do you think you could ask him to stop in at Brett and Brett's? . . . No, not the one on Forty-second Street, the one at Fifth and Fifty-seventh. . . . That's right, on the corner. Ask him to get me two little brushes for my lighter, very hard ones. They don't know how to make them like that over here. If it's any trouble for him to bring them, he could have them put in the pouch.* . . . What's the weather like over there? We're all freezing here." And so on.†

If I admire the *sang-froid* with which top people can phone New York to ask for two little brushes for a cigarette lighter as if it were a message of the utmost urgency to be transmitted by a cable running across the ocean bed, it's because I for my part would never dare do such a thing in front of six or eight other people. This simply proves that I haven't the grand qualities of a top man any more than the sublime detachment which, only an hour after such a conversation, will enable him to dictate a note designed to

---

* *Diplomatic, of course.*
† *Such conversations take place in big company offices, where they are charged to general expenses. At home they are much briefer.*

stamp out the gross abuse which the staff makes of the telephone for private purposes during office hours.

To return to my current president–director general, M. de Stumpf-Quichelier,* I hardly have occasion to meet him other than in the corridor, save for exceptional circumstances. Our exchange of remarks is always the same. I say, "Good morning, Monsieur le Président," and he, without stopping, replies in a half-protective, half-authoritarian tone, "Morning, Blot" (though sometimes he forgets my name), "how goes it? I'm counting on you!" This, together with "We need miracles, miracles!" is one of the chief's pet formulas. He uses it regularly whenever he passes a department head or branch manager whom he doesn't otherwise have occasion to see. Familiar to the whole office, this "How goes it? I'm counting on you!" is broken up into two parts and spoken in two different tones which have become traditional. "How goes it?" or "Well, how goes it?" is pronounced in a shrill, nasal tone which brooks no opposition, like the "Well, is the soup good?" of a general; it goes without saying that the president–director general, despite his "Well?," has neither the time nor the inclination to know that all isn't well. Besides, this "How goes it?" is accompanied by a forward thrust of the chin and a pouting of the lips, curled up to the nostrils, which make it perfectly clear to the department head that the chief carries all the petty concerns of the others on his shoulders ("Yes, yes, I know, you have your problems, but

* S.Q. *outside his presence, and to his familiars.*

I have mine which embrace all yours—I know everything that goes on!").* There is a faint pause—the time it takes him to pout. Then, nodding his head, M. de Stumpf-Quichelier releases his "I'm counting on you!" in a graver tone but with a conspiratorial wink: he knows his confidence is not misplaced. By the time the chief has said "I'm counting on you!" he is already far down the hall.

There are some employees (newly promoted or little used to meeting the chief) on whom the "I'm counting on you!," although known to be automatic (he might just as well say, "Pleased to meet you," or "Fine morning"), has considerable effect. So much so that they go about their affairs supercharged, as if S.Q. had delegated his powers to them. There are others on whom the sacred formula has no effect at all—or else provokes a strange reaction. These always recall the case of Perrichet, which has grown into a legend. How could he, Perrichet, have helped being staggered to hear the chief pronounce his "How goes it? I'm counting on you!" on the very same morning he had received a letter telling him he was fired? But how could you really blame the president–director general in a firm as vast as ours for failing to remember every single letter he was given to sign?

". . . *your boss?*"
My real boss is Barnage, codirector general with wall-to-

---

* *People so often say to the chief, "Don't you waste your time on that, Chief. So-and-So will see to it!" or "You have too much on your hands to attend to that, Chief. Let X settle the matter!" that I wonder what there is left for him to do.*

wall carpeting, wall-to-wall drapes, four windows and two private secretaries. But it's time for me to explain the hierarchy of the building. With us the importance of a colleague can be measured by the size of his room. Firstly, there are those who work in huge glass cages; they are legion and their slightest movement can't fail to escape the eye of the head of their department, isolated in his transparent cell. This total lack of privacy—comparable to that of a goldfish in its bowl or of those girls who sit invisibly mending in shop windows before the gaze of every passer-by (I wonder what sadistic pharaoh of the shop world could have thought up that idea)—is one of the happy discoveries of the modern world. The transparent beehive is a perpetual torment to the junior staff, who cannot even scratch their noses or sneak a piece of chocolate out of their desks without a feeling of being spied on. You become somebody in the organization only from the moment when, having escaped first from the glass cage and then from all the combinations of multiple offices without armchairs, desk lamps, windows, secretaries or carpeting, you're installed, invisible and alone, behind a mahogany desk in a room with red leather armchairs, to which your secretary has access only when summoned.

This, of course, doesn't apply to the big chief, who, alongside his command post, has had himself fixed up with a sort of Empire boudoir which resembles practically anything except an office. Flowers are not a privilege exclusive to Stumpf-Quichelier, but in order to have a right to flowers you must wait for him to give the word. Thus

Luchard had to wait for two years, Pignatel for three. One day the chief said, "Ah, you're admiring my flowers, eh? But you yourself have a great many people calling on you— why don't you get some too?" Permission thus being granted, one puts out flowers—less beautiful than the chief's and changed only once a week. To my knowledge, there are four higher-ups who have a right to flowers "like the chief."

What wouldn't one do in the image of S.Q.? There exists with us a rather peculiar sort of mimicry. There's nothing particularly astonishing about the fact that, after eighteen years in his service, Mlle. Farjeau, S.Q.'s secretary, should have finally acquired his features and should present the aspect of an elderly and battered bulldog (the same osmosis can be seen in more than one old married couple). What I find more surprising is the extent to which M. de Stumpf-Quichelier's closest colleagues, doubtless by dint of living in close contact with him and under his thumb, adopt his attitudes, tone of voice and mannerisms, whether it be his way of nibbling the ends of his glasses as he leans back in his chair, his habit of pushing up these glasses on his forehead like a racing driver when he pulls in to refuel, his passion for ending his questions with "*quoi?*—what?," or even a sort of salivary hiss he makes by pressing his tongue against the roof of his mouth. One cannot positively assert that this mimicry was in its origins unconscious. Conscious mental control still limits it in certain instances; it is inconceivable, for instance, that Barnage should push his glasses up on his forehead in S.Q.'s presence, or that Lucot, when with him, should make the same noise with his tongue. But what is certainly true is that, after a managerial conference, five or six colleagues will all go off, each to his office, and spontaneously repeat the chief's gestures, words, grimaces and byplay with the eyeglasses before ten other people. Whether they like it or not, it leaves an indelible mark on them of which they are no longer aware.

Together with the wall-to-wall carpeting and the wall-to-wall drapes, one quickly recognizes other distinctive signs of power in Barnage: on his desk, a photograph of Mme. Barnage (among such privileged higher-ups it is usually the children who are displayed under glass—large-size pictures if they're small, small-size if they're large; the wife, considered too mature, has a right only to a small snapshot, if not to complete effacement; but Mme. Barnage, being very pretty, figures on a large scale), a row of telephones, an intercom and a special thermostat whose needles, ultra-sensitive to heat and humidity, indicate at the point where they intersect the temperature at which the room must be maintained for one to enjoy a sensation of ideal well-being.

Barnage often summons me to his office, either directly ("Hello, Blot? Come in for a minute, will you?") or through a secretary ("Monsieur Blot, conference in Monsieur Barnage's office."* This weapon of power—making

---

Despite my penchant for figures, it would be hard for me to state exactly the number of conferences to which I've been summoned since I joined the firm. Six thousand approximately. As these six thousand conferences,

people come to him instantly—he wields to the hilt. The characteristic of omnipotence being not to be sent for by anyone and to be able to send for everyone, M. de Stumpf-Quichelier is akin in this to the President of the Republic. Between the omnipotent, subtle struggles for precedence go on by means of intermediaries. In the old days, top people waged war with each other from their coaches or sedan chairs and demanded an army of lackeys to make way for them. Today they wage war by telephone. Or, rather, they have it waged by their secretaries. It's a question of who doesn't pick up the instrument first. "Get me Monsieur de Stumpf-Quichelier," says M. Ragondeaux, who won't stand for being kept waiting. As M. de Stumpf-Quichelier, annoyed by being kept waiting, has given identical instructions to his secretary, it is finally the secretaries who speak to each other: "Connect me with Monsieur de Stumpf-Quichelier. . . . I'm putting you through to Monsieur Ragondeaux." This exchange having protected their susceptibilities, M. de Stumpf-Quichelier and M. Ragondeaux can proceed to speak to each other in person.

The other day, Barnage summoned me to his office together with Michaud and Goguet. It was for neither a chat nor a conference. In fact, it was for nothing, for

---

averaging an hour each, most often had for their sole outcome the urging of their participants to bring the problem up again in a different form on the occasion of another conference at a higher level, you can calculate the amount of statutory time wasted in nearly three years. Conferences are nonetheless repeated every day with the same portentousness; they must be regarded as one of the favorite office pastimes, a necessity of the modern animal.

Barnage had nothing to say which called for our presence. But he had need of an approving circle while he dictated a memorandum to his secretary. Barnage adores showing off his authority by means of memoranda; it's a sort of psychic release. And he isn't completely at ease unless there are five or six people to hear him. (Sometimes he even sends for me when he has a visitor with him. I make as if to back out, apologizing. "No, no! Don't go, Blot! You can stay. Monsieur X, let me introduce M. Blot, my actuary. He'll be able to give you the figures I can't quite remember." My arrival has put Barnage at ease. He makes me revolve like a cogwheel whose movements he controls. I have become his thing.)

Really and truly, he should have been an actor; his life is made up of performances which he stages to dazzle others and also himself. He is permanently playing a part. Possibly he is himself for a few seconds in the morning, when he wakes up, but he flees from his own self at once. For his wife, the pretty Mme. Barnage, he puts on his first act, at the telephone (the telephone and secretaries being this actor's principal props): the international man of affairs who, before reaching an important decision, takes the pulse of the various capitals. He calls the finance department: "No news from London? . . . New York still calm? . . . Keep an eye on Iraq, it might turn out important. Whom do we have out there?" He knows, but prefers to appear not to. "He's a fool." To listen to Barnage, the world is peopled with fools. "Keep me posted. If trouble blows up, send out Rameille or Valguet. Get me Blot!" After this first act, I can readily picture Barnage playing another with his children: the overburdened man who finds time to mend his son's electric train. If at this moment he gets a call from the office, he is quite happy to reply that his children come before Iraq. Having switched into a third routine (bonhomie, protective familiarity) with his chauffeur, Barnage arrives, already thoroughly played in, on the stage of his principal theater: the company.

That day, then, Barnage made us come in and proceeded to begin as follows: "I believe I am right in saying" —one of his favorite formulas—"that certain departments are failing to reply at all, or at best only after a considerable delay, to requests from clients for information. It's high time this was changed." On the intercom: "Jeanine!

"Jeanine, will you take down a memo for all heads of departments? And I mean *all*, is that clear? Copies to the directors general."

The sending of the memo, so far as we are concerned, is perfectly useless, since we are present, but it is intended to convey a show of condescending politeness toward inferior colleagues.

"It has come to my notice from several sources—no, cut that. No, on second thought, leave it in. It has come to my notice from several sources that"—here a little playful toying with a silver pencil—"that certain departments are failing to reply to clients comma or potential clients comma with either the necessary speed comma or with adequate precision period paragraph. These are failings which I must qualify as unpardonable comma even if they have sometimes been unintentional comma and as causing considerable harm to our company period. I would like it made clear that as of today every letter must be answered within forty-eight hours of its arrival and every client who visits this office whoever he may be, underline 'whoever he may be,'—no, cut that, it makes 'may be may be'—and that every, underline 'every,' client who visits this office is to be received with maximum consideration period. Heads of departments will be held directly responsible for any failure to carry out these elementary rules of politeness."

After which Barnage turned to us with a smile. "They should understand that all right, shouldn't they, what? No?"

Goguet was the first to approve abjectly: "It's a bit . . . Your memo is pretty sharp, M'sieur Barnage!"

"Well, haven't I made my meaning clear?"

"Oh, by all means!"

"I haven't been too tough, what?"

"Oh no, monsieur, it will do them good!"

Barnage to the secretary, as if emboldened by this success: "Type me out a special copy for the president. There, gentlemen, you may go. Oh, Jeanine! Remind me this evening that I have to dine with Lamoricière. What a nuisance! However, it may turn out useful. And get me Wepler in London—I'd like a couple of words with him before that letter goes."

Barnage has been careful to let us know that he has to dine with the Finance Minister. To hear him refer to

"Lamoricière" anyone would think they were close friends, whereas he is really visiting the Minister's house for the first time. And he has made a point of asking his secretary to remind him of this unprecedented event as if, amidst so many obligations of so many kinds, he might possibly forget it. He enjoys being reminded of something he knows by heart, provided it's something that flatters him. On his desk, kept spick-and-span, several high-flown invitation cards are always in evidence—"The British Ambassador and Lady Huttington request the pleasure of the company of Monsieur and Madame Barnage at a reception to be held on the occasion of the visit of Her Majesty the Queen (evening dress, decorations)." If the current month has not proved fertile in cards of this nature, he displays those of the month before.

After this classic interlude, we left Barnage alone with his secretary. Far from ceasing to dictate memoranda, he chooses this time (my information service is well organized) to confirm his power to himself by dictating draft letters addressed to people more powerful than himself, which, however, will never reach their destinations, or only in a very adulterated form. Couched in the style of ultimatums, these letters give Barnage a fleeting but rather pleasant sensation of omnipotence. How many victories does he thus win every day over his secretary, whom he threatens with his epistolary thunderbolts as if she were the president-director general or the Minister for Foreign Affairs, and whose docile, submissive hand nervously transcribes these dictatorial thoughts? No one knows. What we do know, on the other hand, is the style of these autocratic missives, which abound in imperfect subjunctives. Barnage never fails to slip one in whenever he can, and, like all people who use the imperfect subjunctive a great deal, he puts in too many:

"Firmly determined for my own part not to modify my line of conduct comma nor that of the company comma by one atom—no, cross that out—by one iota comma I should be grateful if in future it might be quite clearly understood that any pressure on our departments comma from whoever it might come comma—come in, yes, *come in!* . . . no, don't go, *don't go!*—will meet with a flat refusal period. I cannot see how our reflections might be maintained other than on this basis comma and this basis alone period paragraph. I hardly need to point out that if no conciliatory reply has reached me within a week comma I might find myself under the painful comma but imperative comma obligation of reconsidering the whole question dash were it to be—I said 'were it to be'—on the next occasion with a less favorable eye" (conspiratorial wink at Jeanine). "I hope they'll understand. Read it back."

Halfway between the wall-to-wall carpeting of the top people and the glass cage of the lower orders, far from flowers but quite close to indirect lighting, I maintain myself on that middle path which was destined to me from birth. I sometimes think of the old joke about the well-to-do bourgeois who used to dream of being sufficiently rich or sufficiently poor to be able to do a great many things which were forbidden to him in his comfortable situation. One might say of my profession of actuary what newspapermen say of theirs: that it can lead to everything provided you get out of it. In fact, there are two kinds of actuary: those who remain actuaries and those who are no longer actuaries because they are worth something better. I belong to the first category. I have my ideas, ideas which reach out beyond the framework of actuarihood—but people take them from me.

"People" means, above all, Gaslin, another of my superiors, the assistant director general, who worms his way as often as he can between Barnage and me. Gaslin is a great consumer of ideas. I'm not saying he doesn't have any himself, but he owes a large part of his success to the way in which he chews over the ideas of others.

When I take an idea to Gaslin it never seems to please him. Not, at least, at the time. What I suggest seems utterly superfluous and without any interest; Gaslin doesn't even appear to listen to it. He embarks on another subject immediately. There is my idea, dead and buried. A few days go by, and then, during some conference, Gaslin rises to speak. "It has occurred to me that it wouldn't perhaps be a bad thing . . ." (for which read "I have considered it would be excellent")—and what do I see brought out in public in Gaslin's clothes? *My* idea, the 808, a new combination of complete life insurance with multiple options and repayment of the total premiums paid out.

This habit of annexing other people's ideas, of digesting them for about a week and then producing them as original creations, has reached a pitch where Gaslin is no longer aware of it. He no doubt acts in perfect good faith when he launches "his" idea in public: he has completely forgotten where it came from. This proves he has acquired one of the trump cards of top people: a bland unawareness.*

Thus, willy-nilly, I return to my own little niche of mortality statistics and stick to my place, barely making a feeble attempt from time to time to shake off the yoke of Makeham's law and probability curves. How many times have I seen young wolves come into the office, eager to change everything, their brains seething with new ideas! It lasts one year, two years—the time they themselves take to change. Ah, the noble youth mowed down on the battlefields of these companies, each bringing a soldier's spirit and to receive in return the corpse of an employee! I too walked in one day for the first time, all fire, all flame. I learned my lesson. Today, at about ten to twelve, at about a quarter to six, I look at my watch, knowing full well that when a man begins to look at his watch in an office, he has

---

* This unawareness can manifest itself in a thousand different ways. M. de Stumpf-Quichelier had assembled a few modest heads of departments together on the occasion of a small New Year's celebration. Following I forget what twist, the conversation turned to the standard of living. Each of them in turn (perhaps with some ulterior motive) complained of the ceaseless rise in the cost of living. In order to switch to a lighter topic, someone asked the chief, who is a great sportsman, whether he had shot many pheasants. "Quite a few, quite a few," he replied. "But you were speaking just now about the standard of living. Well, now, my father had two thousand acres with five gamekeepers, whereas I, today, have a mere two hundred with one wretched man. That shows the rise in the cost of living!"

reached the same point as a married man when the only thing he thinks going to bed is for is reading the paper.

"Do you like your work?"

Shall I confess? There are mornings when I'm sick of it, mornings when I haven't the slightest desire to take up where I left off the day before. (For millions of men life is just that. For six days they have no desire to live the day ahead—and the seventh, that Sunday which it is less a question of living than of killing, is worse than the other six.)

On these mornings, I think of the "for me's." I'm sick of "for me." I'd give anything not to hear Barnage any longer bark, "See that you don't forget to review those schedules for me!" When Barnage, having summoned me to his office ("Get Blot for me!"), says, "'See that it's ready for me by this evening!" or "Work out for me the number of potential casualties* for the next year," I get the impression—a painful one—of no longer belonging either to myself or to mankind, but to M. Barnage. The eternal "Do it for me tomorrow without fail!" implies a state of submission, of subordination, which evokes the schoolteacher's "I want you to write out a clean copy for me!" and the sergeant's "Shine this for me on the double!" Doubtless this is the lot of an infinite number of citizens: the barracks of life. This resemblance to a barracks is all

---

* *Every profession has coined words for itself which raise up a barrier against the profane. Just as a newspaperman refers to articles as "copy," a publicity man to newspapers as "outlets," a diplomat to the Ministry of Foreign Affairs as "the Department," so an insurance man speaks of an accident as a "casualty."*

the more evident in our company, where, leaving generals aside, one rises up through the ranks from a humble employee to an assistant section head, then head of a section, assistant to the head of a department, chief deputy department head, head of department, assistant branch manager, to be finally named branch manager.

The "for me," what's more, is not a privilege of only the chief and the heads of departments. The "for me" is contagious. It propagates itself like a sore on the lips, from top to bottom of the office, from the president-director general's "We're lagging behind, gentlemen. You must work miracles for me!" down to that of the attendant on the ground floor ordering the messenger boy, "Take this envelope to the bank for me. It's a rush job, get it? Don't let me catch you stopping off for a drink on the way!"

This corporal's "for me" reflects the same lust for power as the "for me" of the V.I.P. Both men have the company under their skins. Saral, our financial director, will declare, "I've just made a profit of twelve million," as if it were his own money, and I've heard Gillet, the head attendant, reply to a visitor, "Our real-estate office? But that's no longer here. Oh, you didn't know? But yes. You know the big building on the Boulevard Haussmann where the Americans of NATO used to be? Well, we bought it—four hundred and fifty million. That's where they are now."

Gillet retailed all this quite naturally. It does this man good to say "It cost us four hundred and fifty million." (He doesn't translate into new francs, as that wouldn't have the same effect.) One takes one's pleasure where one finds it, even in keeping visitors waiting, the sole witnesses, or almost, of one's mite of authority: "Take this up for me at once to Monsieur Lebrun!"

In short, there are mornings when I would give anything not to have to go through the whole of yesterday again, make the same gestures, hear the same remarks, breathe the same smells and, above all, *above all,* see the same faces. The problem of faces has always haunted me. Faces even manage to wreck my vacation. In summer, in the hotels, what bores me most is to see the same faces at the same tables in the dining room every day for a whole month. (I don't doubt that the others feel equally bored by seeing mine.) At home there are days when I'd like not even to hear the sound of a voice or meet another tenant. Rather than take the elevator with one of them, I slow down or quicken my pace in order to go up alone. Our elevator suffers from that hydraulic lethargy which constrains you to find a topic of conversation. The weather, the heating, the stairs, the rent—it's sheer agony. And for what? Something simply tells me I have to speak to the person who is going up with me.

In an elevator as in salons, not only am I embarrassed if I say nothing, but I'm embarrassed for the other people if they find nothing to say. Summer saves us with the heat, winter with the cold and the flu; in the intervals, when the weather inspires no comment, there always remains, in our building, the cabbage: the place reeks of cabbage. The Butards, second floor left, have been eating it three times a

41

week for the past fifteen years, and the smell of cabbage has impregnated the whole building, with peak periods on Mondays, Wednesdays and Fridays. I honestly believe I would come home in a better temper if it weren't for that stink of cabbage. But, from the very entrance, its flaccid effluvia bear down on me and my energy melts away in the stale warmth of the Butards' cabbage. Possible subjects of conversation in the elevator: we ought to draw up a petition; "they" might put out deodorizers; it shouldn't be allowed; it isn't legal for a building to be condemned to cabbage for life just because one of the tenants likes it; and so on. Again, you must never refer to Butard in person and you must also find responsive people to speak to. (There are some tenants who seem to have no noses and others who are evidently without ears, since they seem never to be bothered by the sounds which get on your nerves.) I did one day have the courage to say to Butard, "Ah, you at least, Monsieur Butard, like cabbage!," hoping by this oblique hint to settle the matter amicably. "Each to his taste, each to his taste," he replied with an equivocal smile—and he left me in the elevator with his smell of cabbage.

When there is really nothing to say about the weather or the building or cabbages, I jingle my keys, whistle through my teeth, do anything, as if by remaining totally passive— even though that would be the natural way to behave—I might lead my companion to think me hostile or imbecile. That's how man is made. He behaves differently in an elevator according to whether he's alone or with somebody

42

else, just as he's not at all the same on entering a restaurant when it's full as when it's empty.

Anyway, all this is nothing. The faces of the tenants, of the concierge—all these faces are transitory. You leave them on the ground floor or the third. There are others which you never leave.

To marry a face and see it every morning and evening for fifty or sixty years is already quite something. But to be wedded to three hundred of them and be condemned to see them for eight hours a day for half a century is really too much for one man. For life in the office is a monstrous marriage with two or three hundred faces. To know in advance what a woman will say, what her reaction will be, what will make her laugh, what will annoy her, why she will sulk—no doubt all that is fairly trying. But to know in advance the expressions three hundred people will have, the words they'll speak, the gestures they'll make, the smells they'll exude—that sometimes seems to me beyond my strength.

To combat this evil of faces, top people have a weapon: their right hands—I mean their right-hand men. These mistress-men, renewable every three or four years and brought in under the label of technical advisers or assistant directors, shooting stars snatched at fabulous sums from some rival firm or parachuted from the lofty spheres of politics, high-society dilettantes up to their ears in smart connections, big talkers, fine swimmers, destroyers of principles, devourers of budgets, blowers of smoke, donors of ideas, inventors of ostentatious expenditure—they are the

43

jesters of these modern kings, their Prince Charmings, their Machiavellis.

"Let me introduce Hubert de Fitz-Arnold, my right-hand man."

Hubert de Fitz-Arnold, with whom began the reign of automation in our office and to whom the company owes the acquisition of an electronic robot costing a thousand million francs, capable of making 600,000 additions in sixty seconds and of reading the Bible in eight and a half minutes, is the fourth right-hand man Stumpf-Quichelier has had to my knowledge. Hubert's great idea is personalized, or, rather (to use a term which flourishes on all our lips), "functional" insurance. Gone are those anonymous policies which took no account of the peculiarities of each holder, but applied equally well to a garage owner in Dunkirk as to a wine grower in Perpignan. And, to begin with, we no longer say "policy" but "program": a program of guarantees which enables the company to cut for the insured, according to his requirements and resources, the suit of protection which best fits him.

Fitz-Arnold's influence has not only introduced a new vocabulary but modified the ways of the agents. The "approach to the prospect"—translate: the siege of the potential client—obeys strict laws laid down in a notice entitled "The Telephone Contact." Life insurance has to be sold like a fur coat or a face cream, and one has to know how to speak of death in the most lively fashion. Rule 1: It is formally forbidden to say to the prospect, "If you were to die tomorrow . . . ," for this supposition, which is gratuitous, has an element of unpleasantness. By saying to him, "If you had died yesterday . . . ," one puts forward a hypothesis which, being formally denied by the facts, engenders in the prospect a happy sensation of security.

This kind of nuance—of which M. de Stumpf-Quichelier himself says, "It's nothing—and it's everything!"—has contributed not a little to the favor in which Hubert de Fitz-Arnold basks. For the moment it is the honeymoon stage. Nothing is done or undone in the building without Hubert's assent. The chief can no longer do without him. At night he wakes Hubert up at the drop of a pin. Hubert is his thing, his echo, his conscience. If Hubert isn't there when there is a decision to be taken:

"Where is Hubert?" asks M. de Stumpf-Quichelier as if he has had his toy taken away from him. "Go and get Hubert! Ah! There's Hubert! Tell me, my dear Hubert . . ."

"Yes, Chief?"

"What do you think, Fitzu" (the diminutive used by the president on his good days), "of this plan for a summer conference for our agents?"

Fitzu purses his lips.

"What? Eh? Yes," growls the chief.

It's enough: the project is condemned. In this honeymoon phase, the slightest reticence on Fitzu's part carries more influence than any circumstantial report from the oldest and trustiest member of the firm. The most firmly established financial program, the most skillfully prepared publicity campaign, can in a flash be overthrown, condemned, made ridiculous by a word from the favorite.

Where does Hubert get his power from? Doubtless from the very power his charm exerts on V.I.P.s. It's largely to him, people say, that M. de Stumpf-Quichelier owes his having finally been promoted to commander of the Legion of Honor. The initial strength of these right-hand men comes from their discretion. Very little is known about their backgrounds. Many of them—like Hubert—are former École Polytechnique boys who, having left the public service, are enjoying slippered ease in insurance. But the great school isn't indispensable to their advancement. They belong to a privileged race, spared by life from the back stairs and from having to start at the bottom and rise by promotion. A certain mystery hovers over their success; it envelops the activities and even the private lives of these gray eminences. They are the Princes of the Wind. It's the wind which brings them ("parachuted" is not an empty word), it's the wind of new ideas which they cause to blow through the petrified structures of long-established firms, it's the wind which bears them away. And when they have vanished, nothing is left of them but what brought them: wind.

How does one succeed thanks to wind? How does the wind make them powerful, respected, feared? Whether it be in industry, banking or insurance, the method the Princes of the Wind follow is roughly the same:

1. Reverse the established order as a matter of principle. Fitz-Arnold is a master at this game. It's enough for him to be presented with a plan spaced out in ten stages for

him to show with a visionary's clear-sightedness that the tenth should be the first. To such an extent that in order to get their suggestions accepted certain colleagues have formed the habit of presenting them to him in a sequence exactly the opposite of what they have in mind.

2. Magnanimously create new items of expenditure. No one would believe with what ease the great company owners, who boggle at an increase of two hundred new francs in an employee's salary, devote two million to putting some idea of their favorite's into action—which favorite, moreover, counts only in hundred thousands. This hasn't failed to happen with Fitz-Arnold. By way of thanking its provincial agents, the company traditionally invited them to spend ten days in a palace in the south of France, rented for the occasion (summer conference). Fitz-Arnold found this banal. Why not hire a liner? And so the president, more than ever in Hubert's wake, decided to take all our agents on a cruise to Naples. See Naples and sell life insurance—could there be a more excellent idea? Costly, but in the long run very profitable.

3. Find the chief's ideas "wonderful," since they, the Princes, are their authors.

One day, however, the chief will have had enough of this face; he will change it. The whole firm believed Hubert de Fitz-Arnold's reign to be near its end when the electronic computer, charged with making a statement of the company's assets, "spat up," as the delighted Goguet put it, "one zero too many" and registered a credit balance of eight thousand million when it was in fact only eight hundred. After an inquiry and an operation carried out by the electronic surgeons, it was discovered that the error came from a magnetic band most provokingly impressed by the flash bulb of a reporter who had come to photograph the wonder. It was a close shave, but Fitz-Arnold is hanging on. Waiting for the time when, repudiated, he will retire to a distant marshalship which the president will have fixed up for him in order to avoid having any longer to see this face which at one time he couldn't do without.

P.S.—To think that I'll have to sum all this up by "Yes" and "No," "Now and then," "Moderately" and "62.5 per cent," on a standard-size postcard! It is one of the manias of our age to want to inaugurate everything in the form of a digest.

3

THE DAILY ROUND

(continued)

7. No doubt good feeling reigns in your home, but there must be some failings with which you reproach women in general and your wife in particular. What are those which seem to you her most characteristic shortcomings, those about which you complain the most?
8. What are the grievances that your wife voices to you most often?
9. Are you . . .

THE THING for which my wife most often reproaches me is being what I am—middle-class. Whether it has to do with the children's upbringing, the way I dress or my reactions to office intrigues, I always hear the same remark:

"Poor Paul, you're so middle-class!"

I can't see what there is about the words "middle class" that is so derogatory that many middle-class people have a horror of being called middle-class. Are people always annoyed at being taken for what they are? From hearing one

49

of the snobs I see on this beach tell a neighbor, "I find him a bit snobbish," it's clear that everyone is a snob—except him.

I have gradually come to believe that a multitude of people hate nothing so much as being called by their own names. The middle class has a horror of being called middle-class, the capitalists have a horror of being called capitalists, peasants peasants, Jews Jews, laborers laborers, soldiers soldiers, rich rich, dentists dentists, idlers idlers, existentialists existentialists, politicians politicians, crooners crooners, aristocrats aristocrats, janitors janitors. Do you ever see an average Frenchman take pride in being an average Frenchman? The average Frenchman is everyone except himself. Whether one is little, average or big, the desire is first and foremost to be neither little, average nor big.

Letter carriers, aghast at being called letter carriers, have succeeded in having themselves baptized "mail superintendents." Moving men, who would consider themselves insulted if you didn't give them something, have managed to have the offensive word tip excised from the professional vocabulary. An archduchess will make it a point of honor to pass for "very unassuming," a pork butcher for "very distinguished." The moment some man really makes a success of marketing cheese or wine, he rushes to commission some eminent man of letters to write a booklet, which he publishes at vast expense under the title *Roquefort's Royal Past* or *Conversations with Claret*. To see, in addition, a mustard manufacturer so tickled by ennoblement that he has a crown emblazoned on his delivery trucks ("The King of Mustards, the Mustard of Kings"),* one can only conclude that the delicatessen business gives rise to complexes at least as much as does royalty. Whereas the mustard maker bills himself as King, a king, a real one, enters a tennis tournament under the pseudonym "Mr. G———"; we learn that the visitor who has taken rooms at the Palace Hotel in St.-Moritz under the name "Monsieur Dupin" is really Archduke Rudolf of Hapsburg (yet another way of attracting attention); we see princes in dungarees, monarchs on bicycles, queens in blue jeans. So much so that we would be within our rights to wonder if the only thing left is to make a gigantic reclassification of society, since society as it is wants to pass for something different.

A journalist of genius, fearing he will be buried as a mere journalist, will always try to prove that he is a bad writer. A great novelist loves, late in life, to be endowed with the sweet name of poet. At the end of his career a comedian finds it hard to resist proving he can do something serious, just as an actor who has become famous as a sinister villain will struggle to show he can excel as a romantic hero. A historian who has devoted his life to the origins of the Middle Ages would think himself belittled if his friends didn't guarantee that he has an unrivaled sense of humor. A general who has made a distinguished career in tanks dreams of having a chair in the Académie Française. There are people ranked as intellectuals who will die without having ever once said, "I am an intellectual." There are

*Crowns flourish equally well on refrigerators, men's shirts, cars or fabrics.

even certain Frenchmen who, when abroad, are afraid of being taken for French and exclaim on sighting a group of compatriots, "More French!" and plunge hastily into conversation with Czechs or Turks—with anybody, in fact, save a Frenchman. Even in Paris you have only to sit down at a restaurant table to hear a Frenchman say, "The French adore that!" or "You'll never get the French to admit that!"—as if he himself were outside the terms of reference. French he is, to be sure, and he would be the first to make a show of it if any doubt were cast on his origins: "I, Monsieur, am a Frenchman!" But to line himself up with Frenchmen in general, with modern Gaul—not on your life!

And so man revolves, casting off the label that has been affixed to him in order to pin it on the back of the next man.

I keep mine for myself, without boasting of it, without denying it. But Thérèse—all in all, wouldn't you say she's the more middle-class of the two of us?

I who am all day long the slave of mathematical forecasts and spend the best part of my time trying to pin down chance in order to deprive it of any chance to operate —I wouldn't have been averse, at home in the evenings, to a little abandon, a certain unexpectedness, even a slightly bohemian disorder. By contrast, I would have found in it the pleasure of a relaxation. I had to abandon any such hope in next to no time. Thérèse has a mania for order and tidiness. In our apartment nothing is ever left lying about.

I leave a newspaper on the bed; I return: the paper is in the rack in the living room. I put down my keys on the table in the hall; I come back to get them: they have vanished into a drawer. I'm scarcely allowed to deposit the ash of a cigarette in an ashtray: it's never the right one. And as for letting the ash fall on the carpet, I get called a savage and see that hateful vacuum cleaner arrive within a matter of seconds.

I used to think I had got involved with a unique specimen. A comedian has since taught me that there exists at least one other like her. I forget now where I heard him, but he had gone through the same hell as I. But he, lucky man, could put it in the past tense. He too had a wife who took out the vacuum cleaner for every scrap of ash. He too could never have the faintest stain on his jacket without his wife's running over immediately with a bottle of cleaning fluid, a cloth and a wire brush—"Get up, not like that, if you stand with your back to the light I can't see, turn around, keep still," etc. He too could never find a paper where he had left it. Her crowning achievement he revealed as follows: "One night, about four in the morning, as I had a headache, I went to take an aspirin in the bathroom. When I got back, my bed was made!"

". . . *her most characteristic shortcomings* . . ."

With Thérèse, the passion for order and cleanliness disappears the moment it's no longer a matter of household affairs. I don't believe it's possible for anyone to show a greater lack of precision in speech or a greater confusion of memory. As proof of this I need only cite the question of names.

There are, I know, certain basic feminine confusions. When a woman mentions Rio de Janeiro, it's an almost safe bet she means Buenos Aires. Thérèse is like this. No one is her equal at confusing Aztecs and Incas, Olympia and Alhambra, Mauriac and Maurois, dynamo and battery, Hawaii and Haiti, Rimski-Korsakov and Rachmaninoff, latitude and longitude, stalactites and stalagmites, Auteuil and Longchamp, Verlaine and Rimbaud, Syria and Lebanon, Scottish and Irish, opal and topaz, Renoir and Degas, Bucharest and Budapest, dolmens and menhirs—but it's all right, I have no objection. And let her go on using *deprecate* for *depreciate, ingenious* for *ingenuous, collaborate* for *corroborate.* I've lived with her long enough to understand what she means.

But when she is given a name on the telephone—a single, simple name—and, starting from this name, she concocts twenty others without ever managing to recapture the name in question, that really gets me down. Let's say, for instance, that it's M. Delestraing. M. Delestraing telephones while I'm out and leaves his name, which he takes the trouble to spell. I'll find a note telling me to call up Delestraint, Delestrin, Delestrain—never Delestraing.

She remembers the people we know, of course. The only thing she forgets is their names. Thérèse's brain is inhabited by a considerable number of names and faces—but if she remembers a face she mislays its name, and if she recalls a name she loses the face that bears it. Once every day, or, more precisely, every evening (Thérèse's memory prefers to wander off every night after eight), my wife, with the excuse that I'm a statistician, consults me as if I were the telephone directory. She has to have a name, the name of someone very familiar to us.

"Isn't it idiotic! I know it as well as my own!"

The name is running through her head, it's on the tip of her tongue—but she can't lay her hand on it. I must help her. For her, for twenty years, I have sought for so many names to give to faces that I have often yearned to live on a planet where there are nothing but nameless faces.

"By the way,"* she'll ask me, "do you know whom I met this morning?"

". . ."

"Dessair!"

"Oh, Dessair? I thought he was in Belgium."

"Oh, how stupid I am!† *You* know—a fellow who was at Chamonix. It also begins with a D. Come on, you must remember."

"I don't see—"

"Oh, listen, don't be so stupid. *You* know—he took us out for a drive in his car."

"You don't mean Desclaux?"

---

* When Thérèse says, "By the way," that doesn't mean in the least that there's any connection between what she's about to say and what has just been said.

† By dint of hearing a woman say, "How stupid I am!" you might end by believing yourself entitled to say that she is—but when a woman says, "How stupid I am!" she simply means that her intellect has momentarily faltered.

"No, no! How idiotic! I know it perfectly well. If only you'd help me . . ."

"Listen, darling, I'm trying, but I really can't think whom you mean."

"Oh! You can't think—! It's as clear as a bell, isn't it? The—fellow—who—took—us—out—for—a—drive—at—Chamonix!"

"I can't help feeling it *was* Desclaux—"

"You just keep quiet! You'll be more of a help that way. Just wait while I think. It wasn't Dessouches, Dessair, Duchesne, Dutertre—something rather like Dicter . . ."

"Delvert?"

"*No*, like Dicter! Now you're getting me all mixed up. It's really outrageous the way you can't even help me find a name! Wait—I've got it! His wife had a pony-tail and a red bow."

"Oh, *him!* You should have mentioned that sooner. Tiégler."

"That's it—Tiégler."

"But you told me it began with a D. At that rate I'd never have found it."

"I? You're out of your mind. I never mentioned any D. It was a T."

"But I'm *sure* you said—"

"Now, listen, I can at least remember what I told you only two minutes ago, can't I? I haven't lost my grip to that extent. Are you trying to make me out to be crazy? I do believe you are!"

"This is really too much. I would bet a thousand—"

"This eternal mania for betting! Incidentally, I notice that I only have to mention a woman with a pony-tail for you to immediately remember the name."

"To remember immediately."

"Exactly!"

"No—I said, 'To remember immediately.' To remember the name immediately. Not 'to immediately remember.'"

"Ah! So now you're giving me lessons in grammar! I must say you pick a fine moment."

"Oh, come, Thérèse, you can't be serious. Don't get so worked up. After all, what's all the fuss about? This morning you met Tiégler. Fine. If you tell me you met him, it must be because of something he said to you. Won't you tell me what it was, dear?"

"All right, if you want—but, frankly, you don't deserve to hear it. Well, he said, 'Be sure to tell your husband he must take you without fail to see Ingrid Bergman in . . .' Oh, damn! Now you've upset me, I'm not going to be able to remember the name of the film! At any rate, it's an English film they're showing at the Champs-Élysées."

"That's odd. Offhand, I don't think I— You don't mean *Smiles of a Summer Night?*"

"No!"

"Was it *Wild Strawberries?*"

"Yes, that's it!"

I don't demur, particularly over the fact that it's actually a Swedish film directed by Ingmar Bergman in which Ingrid Bergman doesn't appear. This would only provoke complications. Wiser to keep silent.

Nonetheless I can't help totaling up the colossal amount of time I must have spent hunting for the names Thérèse has forgotten. This happens to her almost every time she decides to tell some story to friends. For my part, I could quite easily forgo the name; the story would neither gain nor lose in interest thereby. But she must have it at all costs. Failing which, she threatens to drop the story itself. (It's always the people whom names elude who seem to set the most store by them.) I then feel myself obliged to come to her rescue, I turn out my memory like an old trunk, out of politeness our friends do the same, and there is the whole table rushing off in pursuit of a name—in vain, because the names we find for her are never those Thérèse is looking for.

After ten minutes of fruitless searching, she says quite simply, "Never mind. The name will come back to me later."

Everyone subsides. The talk turns to other things. Thirty minutes go by, an hour. Then, along about midnight, while someone is hard at it explaining to a rapt audience the unknown facts behind the signing of the Nazi-Soviet Pact in 1939, Thérèse cries, "It was Marilyn Monroe!"

Which pleases everybody, particularly the gentleman with the facts behind the pact.

The oddest thing about it is that Thérèse no longer suffers the faintest lack of memory the moment I myself embark on a story which involves the names of places or dates. If I venture to say, "At Boulogne in 1953 we ate the biggest mussels I've ever seen," Thérèse, recovering all her precision, will interrupt me and declare:

"But no, dear, you've got it wrong. It was at Crotoy in 'fifty-six."

Together with names, nothing haunts Thérèse so much as resemblances.

Every year the same scene is enacted during our vacation. Someone sitting in the hotel lounge reminds her— "But it's incredible how *much* he reminds me . . ."—of someone we met the previous summer in Brittany.

"It's astounding. You remember, his wife had red hair— and an English accent."

"Watrou? The Swiss?"

"No, no, a Frenchman with a red-haired wife and a basset hound."

"Luriez?"

"You're being silly. Anyway, can't you *see?* The resemblance is glaringly obvious."

(Another of those things which stare me in the face and which, of course, I can't see.)

All the names of all the people we met last summer are gone through. My head is nothing but a huge calendar, the pages of which I turn one by one.

Meanwhile Thérèse cries, "Oh, it's just too stupid! The same eyes, the same mouth, the same voice. I've never seen such a likeness! Only his eyes—they're quite different . . ."

In the end I certainly have to agree—it's incredible. No

resemblance could possibly be more striking. After having made me hunt for twenty minutes for the person this man resembles, Thérèse has had a sudden revelation: he resembles himself! This man who so much reminded her of another man is the selfsame man.*

At the start of married life this sort of thing is amusing. At the end of a year, one gets tired of it. After that, it becomes odious.

P.S.—How can all this be translated by "Yes" or "No"? Reading through the notes I've made with this contest in mind, I'm left puzzled as to the best way to reply tersely to the questions asked. My replies will doubtless be: "My middle-classness. Her mania for tidiness; a complete lack of precision over proper names; her inconsistency." But will this provide the necessary information?

---

* Need I point out that the man had neither a red-haired wife nor a basset with an English accent?

4

CONJUGAL LIFE

1. Do you think that Frenchmen
   a. Are good husbands?
   b. Are faithful or unfaithful?
   c. Resist the lure of that famous triangle so often illustrated in films and on the stage?
2. Do you believe in a Great Love?
3. Have you already known such a love?
4. Do you feel that a wife, after several years of marriage, should close her eyes to a husband's love affair?
5. What will be the percentage of divorces in France for the year ending at the moment the contest closes?
6. Are conjugal "scenes" the exception in your home or . . .

"I HOPE YOU aren't going to waste all your time going in for this contest," said Thérèse, seeing me up to my eyes in the newspaper. "Aren't the races enough for you? You'd be better off if . . ."

With Thérèse there's always something I'd be better off doing. I can do fifty thousand things in front of her, none of them is ever the best one. I can't recall that in twenty years of marriage she has once told me that what I was doing was the best thing I could be doing.

It would be very wrong of her to get worked up about it. In the first place, even if this contest leads me to indulge in a little reflection, I still haven't made up my mind to enter it. And if I do, the replies I'll give will amount to nothing compared with what I could have written!

Our life together is identical with the lives of millions of other couples, which sometimes go well, sometimes badly. I think of those of whom the crime reporters say, "They were often heard quarreling." In point of fact, for twenty years our life together has been shaken by only a few storms—and one big one. Yes, there has been a woman in my life. And, as with all men of whom they say, "There's a woman in his life," she wasn't my wife.

"Do you believe in a Great Love?"

If the nature of today's question worries Thérèse, it's because she always has in the forefront of her mind the circumstances of the drama which rocked our union one day—and even more than one. I, outwardly a man so settled, so bourgeois, so transparent! I believe she still hasn't accepted the fact that anyone but she could have noticed me. (Nor have I, for that matter.) True, it was someone very unobtrusive—a secretary. She was called Miriam. She was twenty-six. For me, already in my forties, Miriam was a return of spring. The true miracle of love at that age is that it makes you twenty years younger in a second. One second was enough, when her hand came to rest on mine one evening in the cinema, for me to feel running under my skin that wave of happiness which had lain dormant for so long. A hand, the mere touch of a hand, and everything reeled. I had the impression of being reborn in a different world. That of Miriam was no longer mine: Little Tich and Pears Soap, the Boeuf sur le Toit and Eaude Mélisse, Carpentier, Dempsey, Suzanne Lenglen, Fonck, zeppelins and Bugattis, even Landru and Zaharoff—all these names which had haunted my childhood awoke no responsive echo in her.

I felt myself younger than ever, the citizen of a new country which was called Miriam. Perhaps that is love—to realize that the person one loves has become a new country of one's own? Away from her I was rootless. I no longer breathed the same air, the blue sky was not blue for me. Her face floated ceaselessly before my eyes, it interposed itself between Thérèse and me, it rose up on Barnage's desk, I found it emerging from the electronic computer. Even in the street it haunted me so closely that I was tempted to fit it on other necks. I ached to find again her voice like a waterfall, her silences like a country meadow.

But I must stop. A romantic statistician—that can become dangerous. Besides, why should I explain any further the drama which was let loose? It was so utterly banal! True, in love everything is banal until the day one is caught up in it oneself; then it becomes extraordinary. Anyway, it was a case like millions of others, the eternal story with which the theater regales us every time we visit it. Only, there it is: There on the one hand is life as women read about it in novels, understand it in plays, see it in films— and on the other, quite simply, life. I'm obliged to state that in ordinary life Thérèse will not accept the hundredth part of what she accepts—what am I saying? applauds—in the theater.

Women weep over Anna Karenina, they accept quite readily (at least when it's on the stage) that the father of a family, fascinated by the charms of a young girl, should be consumed by the flames of passion, they tremble for Tristan and Isolde, nothing stirs them to such tenderness as the guilty loves of Julien Sorel and Madame de Rênal, unless it is those of a son with his mother (provided, at least, that the incest is signed by Sophocles). There they sit with their eyes brimming with tears.

"It's love," they say. "It's life!"

But should the husband of one of these women confess one day that he is consumed by the same flame, ravaged by the same yearning, obsessed by the same desire, what then is left of those storms of the heart, of that devastating blaze, that thunderbolt—in short, of Love with a capital L? Nothing. Or, rather, something: That "irresistible inclination," those "tender leanings," those "ecstasies," that "burning desire," all that delirious vocabulary so eagerly devoured in fiction, all those tender phrases so tenderly read or heard, all this adds up to either one or four words: *bed, bed with a tramp.* Tristan is immortal. Tristan is reborn each day, there are throughout the world millions of

Tristans—but not you. However great the purity of your feelings, the violence of your passion, the rendering of your soul, you are nothing else, Tristan, but a *filthy swine*. The famous act of the flesh so nobly hymned by the poets is nothing but an ignominy. Your angel? A bitch! Her caresses? Depravity! As for Love, it is quite simply a bad case of lechery.

It seems that, for married women, there exists only one type of woman with whom their husbands may deceive them: a prostitute. Their best friends, the ones they held up as shining examples, the ones they adorned with all the virtues, the most innocent nymph, a young girl only just born into the sunshine of love, a Danish princess passing through Paris—all become *that tramp, that bitch, that creature*, as soon as they dare to touch their sacred husbands. Contrary to what goes on in books, in the theater or on the screen, it appears to be impossible for a married man to fall in love with a normal woman.

To begin with, it's quite simple: you're not in love. *That little slut* has *turned your head*, unbalanced you. She is the spirit of evil. What proves this is that *there are quite enough bachelors in the world for her not to have to run after a married man!* Love? Pah! It's all a plot. She has taken a pernicious delight in disregarding the baying hordes of men-who-want-nothing-but-that, widowers and divorcés, to attack a happy home. (Never for one moment does it occur to a married woman that "that creature," for her part, might have found it far less complicated to choose

65

a bachelor. *She has done it on purpose.*) "Why do this to me? And why her? Why this particular woman, of all people?"

In my case it was, as I have said, a secretary. But had she been a woman explorer or a fashion model, it wouldn't have changed the situation in any way. The woman you fall in love with is never the one who, in a pinch, might have been accepted as "possible." The "Frankly, I do think you might have chosen someone else!" rings out whoever the chosen one may be. Another thing which gives me food for thought: People talk because bosses fall in love with their secretaries, husbands with their sisters-in-law, wives with their husbands' best friends—but why should you fall in love with someone you never normally see?

However that may be, where is Love in all this?

Love doesn't exist.

This is what emerges very clearly from the classic interrogation,* which begins with the traditional question: "And what might her age be?"

1. *Between twenty and twenty-six:*

---

* *It goes without saying that this isn't based on my own example alone; that wouldn't be enough. I'm relying on a mass of cases which have come to my knowledge, directly or indirectly. I don't know if we should take literally, or, rather, figuratively, the statistics of that public-opinion poll according to which one marriage in every three turns out badly. But I have my own. Life insurance is a confessional which is almost as good as a lawyer's office or a doctor's consulting room for enabling you to know what to make of happiness; of all human enterprises, it shows beyond doubt the biggest deficit.*

66

"Well, I like that! You'll be arrested for corrupting minors next. Are you simply out for sex? Soon you'll be hanging around the schoolyards! Can't you see what a fool you're making of yourself? I might perhaps understand your falling in love with a woman, a real one—but with a child! Twenty! A fine state of affairs, I must say. I know what it was like to be twenty! And how do you suppose it will be in ten years' time? Have you stopped for a minute to think about the next ten years? Eh? They'll make her only thirty, but you'll be fifty-five. You wait and see. She'll drop you flat then, just as you want to drop me now!"

2. *Between twenty-seven and thirty-three:*

"She's afraid of missing the boat. It's as plain as the nose on your face. And you're letting her treat you like a child! After twenty-eight, everyone knows women cling like leeches. But you're such a baby, you can't see a thing. Marriage is what she's out for, it couldn't be more obvious. A fat lot she cares about you!"

3. *Between thirty-four and forty:*

"Well now, really, I just don't understand. I might possibly have a glimmering if you'd fallen in love with a young thing of twenty—but this! And what do you suppose you'll be doing in five years' time, eh? And all because, I imagine, her figure has held up a little better than mine. No doubt because she hasn't worn herself out raising children, of

67

course! In five years'—what am I saying?—in *two* years' time you'll come running to me. You won't find many women in their forties as good as your own wife! Why, only yesterday, in the bus, someone said, 'Excuse me, mademoiselle.' "*

It's hard to see many traces of love in all this—merely the squalid scheming of creatures avid to get their claws into a husband and wrest him from his wife. And even if I manage, by dint of persuasion and frankness ("I'm in love. That's simple enough, isn't it? It's not the first time it has happened."), to convince Thérèse, she immediately cries:

"Even so, in heaven's name, love isn't everything!" (Or "That isn't"—for "that" read "animal instinct.") "You men, you're all the same! You have just that one thing on your minds." (Note that love, when it applied to her, was never thus qualified.) "All you think of is bed. It's the only thing you're interested in. Your wife can kill herself trying to give you a nice home and bring up your children, slaving to cook and keep the house clean, coping with servants—and a hell of a lot any of you care!"†

---

* *The idea that she might have been taken for an old maid never crosses her mind.*
† *At some stage in any scene, Thérèse never fails to put me in the plural. This plural, which springs so spontaneously from her tongue, is strictly forbidden from mine. The least "You women . . ." is best kept in check. If, for instance, I say, "I'm only a man—I'm only doing what millions of men do"—fatal! "Well, if you're going to start taking others as an example, all I can say is you're a fine one to talk!" In short, if she picked me it was because I belonged to a different race. She thought that in me*

So here we are in the center of one of the most vicious of circles. Take love away from a woman and talk to her of tenderness, affection, respect ("I have a deep affection and respect for you"—these two words always come bracketed together), and it will be clear that all this counts for nothing. And yet, on her wedding day, or the eve of it, she had declared (this time in the tenderest possible way), "Besides, love isn't everything. Love can fade, like anything else. But other things are left: tenderness, affection, kindness, respect for each other."

Has the world turned upside down? Have these truths become lies? Today none of that counts any more; the only thing that counts is love. Your tenderness? She doesn't want it. As for respect: "Whom do you think you're talking to—your grandmother?"

On the other hand, leave a woman with nothing but love and she'll soon complain that, apart from that one thing, apart from your animal satisfaction, nothing interests you; you never show her any of those little attentions that make all the difference.

"I don't ask for very much. A little warmth, a little tenderness." (These two again are never pronounced separately.) "But no, nothing. Nothing but *that!*"

Thus one might formulate a general principle: What you give is nothing; what you take is everything.

The minutes I have stolen at the cost of Machiavellian

---

she had found that rare specimen, the man who is different from all other men. That's what every woman believes of the husband she chooses—until the day she puts him in the plural.

scheming are those which would have been the dearest to Thérèse. "It wasn't so very much to ask of you: just that one weekend together."

That weekend—neither the one before nor the one after. The same applies to the place. In twenty years of married life, I have been once on my own to the Riviera; that's the one place she would have liked to be.

As for the element which might in your view make everything easy, it's never the right one. Take money, for example:

1. *You have some:*

"You know very well I'll never desert you," you tell her. "You'll always have everything you need." As you say this, you think of all those cads you know who have left their wives with three children each and who pay them an allowance of 350 new francs a month. You think that your wife will display some awareness of your generosity. An error. A grave error.

"Now, if that doesn't just about take the cake! I won't hear of such a thing! Tell me, do you really suppose I'm going to feel grateful to you just because you're not completely inhuman? You're not going to get away with it so easily, let me tell you!"

"But that isn't what I meant at all, my dear!" (It's never exactly what you meant when you have in fact said exactly what you meant.)

70

"What, then? Your money, always your money! I don't give a damn for your money! That's the only word you ever use: money! Do what you like with your money, your rotten money. Money, money, money!"* And so on.

2. *You haven't any:*

It's very simple: the only thing that counts is money. "So you think you're going to be able to keep two women when you can't even manage with one. So Monsieur takes himself for a millionaire!" And so forth.

Only a playwright knows how to extricate his characters from this sort of vicious circle. As for me, I go round and round without discovering a way out.

In truth, I would give everything I possess to any dramatic author who succeeded, in times of crisis, in working out my own decisive scene in my own home the way he does it on the stage. I'm well aware that this is impossible, just as it's impossible to stage a real domestic quarrel behind the footlights—it would be a dire flop. One says either too much or too little. The only people who know the exact dosage are men of the theater. There everything is crammed into the same act. One decisive remark invokes an incisive reply which provokes a final rupture. Within fifteen minutes, twenty at the outside, everything is settled. At home, the scene may go on for eighteen

---

* *Generally repeated three times.*

months. Each time it has broken out I have had the impression that this was going to be decisive—and each time everything has been left hanging in the air.

Obviously I can't be using the words I should. What is so wonderful in the theater is the way in which the actors find the right words at crucial moments. Take, for example, one or two scenes from famous plays which lead up to a rupture:

We must not hereupon give way to tenderness.
I have sufficient bitterness to fill my heart,
Without you add your tears to torture me still more.

Or:

Listen—I swore on the day I married you that
I would be as pure as the purest crystal. Well—
the crystal is no longer clear.

This is all very pretty, no doubt. "The purest crystal." But just try and bring that out on the spur of the moment. I defy anyone who has a stormy day of reckoning with his wife to express himself in that way. We never say anything remotely like it, not at least all at one try, in the whole of our lives. I don't, at any rate. The words are hard to find. A prompter is needed. Just as the solution you propose is never the right one, the word you use is never the right one. That is doubtless why the leitmotiv of conjugal scenes is that eternally echoing phrase "But that isn't what I meant at all!" What would we think of actors who never stopped repeating, "But, darling, that's not what I meant"?

Then there are sobs, shrieks, hysteria. In the theater, the audience wouldn't be able to hear a thing. On the stage even the sobs are controlled; between hiccoughs the actor finds the necessary resources to say something perfectly valid which furthers the action. In life, on the other hand, everything is disorganized, absurd, tragicomic. One ill-chosen word—and they're all ill-chosen—brings up with undreamed-of-precision what happened one afternoon in 1946 at your mother-in-law's. The opportunity is seized to sift through all the members of your family, who, it must be admitted, don't amount to much.

Not to mention the ill-timed comings and goings of persons before whom you're obliged to change the subject immediately. In the theater, when the crucial scene comes, the interested parties are left alone; no child, no gas inspector, no telephone call arrives to check the development of the plot or interrupt the ping-pong of the dialogue. What would people say if, just as one of the actors cries, "I have sufficient bitterness to fill my heart!" the maid announces the arrival of the laundry? In life, not only is the laundry man's arrival announced, but Thérèse, even at the peak of the most impassioned dispute, won't hesitate for a split second—she'll rush off to count the sheets. There will always be time to talk about divorce afterward. Whether it's the laundry or something else, it never fails: you need only say, "Let's sit and talk things over quietly for ten minutes," and you'll be constantly disturbed.

Nothing is as exhausting as these scenes, whether they're

spasmodic or continuous. You have to be an actor to withstand the blow without flinching and not feel the debilitating effects of battle. With me, they entail a greater loss of energy than two days' solid walking or a week's work. Perhaps because—here again it's the opposite of what happens on the stage, where everything has to be wound up by midnight—the scene, the real one, having broken out the first time after dinner, at about 10 P.M., breaks out all over again in the dead of night, long after all the theaters have lowered their curtains. It would seem that a certain taste for high tragedy and good staging incites women to choose the night to unleash their fury (in daylight, they have a predilection for public places). Thérèse's sobbing wakes me up; I try to calm her. "Why are you crying?" I ask (as if I didn't know). And this question, as stupid as it is futile, lets loose another flood of hysterics, the end of which is rarely to be anticipated before 5 A.M., without the problem's having been taken a single step further. The truth is, the theater is the only place in the world where scenes bring matters to a head. In real life you mark time, you get the feeling that words serve no purpose. Or else the words overrun your thoughts, or you have thoughts which you can't put into words.

For the rest, to speak or not to speak? Here opinions differ. There are those who set up truth as their golden rule and who speak. There are those who raise lies to the level of a cult and admit everything but the truth. There are those who simply drop hints. And those who never speak at all ("Time settles everything.").

I have never yet managed to follow a very determined line. For a long, a very long, time I too raised lying to the level of a moral obligation: lying so as to avoid causing suffering.

Lying, lying all the more when she says, "At any rate, I would rather know. The agony of doubting! Besides, I can't bear the thought of being deceived." (This "besides" ought to be replaced by "above all.")

Alas, all this is false (except for the part about being deceived, for self-esteem and fear of ridicule come before everything else). Women want to know, "know where I stand"—"get to the bottom of it." When they do know, it's never what they wanted. Thérèse is tortured by doubt, it's true, but if there's one thing that tortures her even more it's the truth.

I know this all too well—ever since the day I decided to speak. Speaking serves no purpose before you've decided to make the break. Before that, everything is useless; you admit too much or not enough. That at least is what happens with me. If I speak, I immediately regret what I've said. If I don't, I regret having kept silent.

I had tried everything. I had played the tired husband, the depressed husband, the harassed husband, the husband in torment, the preoccupied husband—even the obsessed husband, the sexual monster, pretending to wake up suddenly in the middle of the night, crying, "Your neck, I want your neck!"

One day I decided to denounce myself: "I've been

75

wanting to tell you for a long time, Thérèse, it's the least I owe you. I'm a monster, you have married a monster. In short, I'm sexually obsessed—I have a passion for braids." I had, on thinking it over, decided that braids were preferable to her neck. I thought I would terrify her, make her long to free herself from the clutches of the monster.

She simply laughed. All this was just a passing fancy, a silly whim. All men have their foibles: black stockings, leather, plastic rainwear, frilly underclothes. "Do you still love me? Have you any feeling for what we've built up together?"

"Oh, come now . . ."

"Then you're not going to leave it all flat for a girl with pigtails, are you?"

Floods of tears, hysterics. Result: nil.

A month later I changed my tactics. I decided to play the moody husband—moody to such an extent that it would be impossible not to ask me if I were worried about something. Then I would speak out, the drama would unleash itself, the decision would become inevitable.

In order to relive a scene, there's nothing like putting oneself back in the atmosphere of the moment. Everything is still vivid in my memory; life became, at one and the same time, both wonderful and suffocating.

Standing before the door of my apartment, I envy those men who, when six o'clock comes around, rub their hands before leaving the office and happily return home, fitting their keys into their doors with contented smiles. That has happened to me, to me too, I reflect. This woman who waits for me behind the door which I now hesitate to open —I used to play games with her. I used to pretend to be a dog; she would hide in a corner of the hall and I would be a big dog sniffing around. Yes, I used to play the dog, and today—today I turn the same key with terror, as if I were unlocking my prison. The only thing that sustains me is the thought that at the same moment millions of men like me, opening the doors of their apartments, would rather be doing anything but getting home. It's of them I think, of all those who are so bored that they'll telephone the girl whose recorded voice tells the time, of all those who wake up in the morning without feeling any temptation to live, of all those who live just as a matter of principle, to keep things going. The number of people who have married and can no longer bear the sight of each other is so great that I sometimes wonder if antipathy is born of marriage, or marriage of antipathy. The attraction of opposite poles is a law, isn't it? But why hold forth on marriage? Everything has been said—even, and above all, by the humorists—whether it be to compare it with a book whose first chapter is written in verse and the rest in prose, or to a meal in which the soup is better than the dessert.

In short, I exude boredom. I look at Thérèse in utter dejection. I sigh when I think of the children. ("My God, the poor children! What will become of them?") I sprawl in my chair. I'm not hungry. A pity: we're having my favorite, sautéed kidneys. But no. Not hungry. Even for kidneys. In fact, my head is full of my plan. During the afternoon, I have seen a friend whose wife, for one, understood that he needed a change. An artist. I'm not an artist, but even in insurance a man may feel a need for a change.

Here we go:

"My, what a long face you're wearing! That's nice and cheerful! I can't say my own day has been exactly a picnic. Anyway, say something, at least. Is anything worrying you? I'm sure it will work out."

(This isn't exactly the way in which I've envisaged the scene beginning, but there's no going back now.)

"Worrying me? Yes and no."

"If you're going to start being difficult . . ."

"Listen, Thérèse. It's better that I should speak to you frankly." (Which seems to imply that I've never spoken frankly for years.) "I'm bored—"

"Well, isn't that splendid! You're bored! Do you suppose that I have a gay time?"

"I'm not talking about you."

"Naturally. Self, self, self! All you ever think of is yourself. All you ever talk of is what you've done. Yourself is the only thing you care about. So, then, Monsieur is bored!"

"Yes. I need—"

"A change of air, no doubt? Well, then, let's go, my dear, let's go! We haven't been anywhere for ages. I'd like nothing better. Look here, next week the children go off for their school camping trip in the mountains. Let's make the most of it. I'd love to see Corsica."

"That's not what I meant. I need to . . . to renew myself."

"Renew yourself! Monsieur wants to renew himself! I must say I find one of you quite enough!"

"This isn't the moment to joke."

"Well, really! This is too much! I suppose it was I who began all this?"

"No, but I mean—"

"Between what you mean and what you don't mean . . ."

"I mean that I need to change my outlook on life."

"In other words, you want to go away. Is that what Monsieur is getting at?" (The husband, in domestic scenes, becomes "Monsieur," pronounced "Môssieu.")

"It is."

"And go alone, naturally."

"Yes."

"The idea! You've always told me that you can't stand being by yourself."

"I've changed."

"So now you'd gladly go away with anyone else but me!"

"I didn't mean that at all—"

"Now, look here, this is getting on my nerves. Just tell me once and for all what you *do* mean and skip the rest."

"Well, I need to renew myself, to have a change of outlook. Look, Jacques has gone off by himself, and his wife—"

"Now, don't mention that man to me. Anyone else, but not him!"

(Another principle: The man you select to hold up as an example is always the one who should never be mentioned.)

"All men feel the need sooner or later."

79

"Need to do what? Blow everything sky high? But go on, say it. Say it, since that's what you're getting at. Leave us! Go, if that's what you want! Let this tramp get her way and break up our home! I'll manage somehow—I'll go out and scrub floors."

"Darling!"

Why scrubbing floors? (And as for that, why "darling"?) Thérèse, like all the rest of them, would be perfectly capable of doing a great many less repellent, more remunerative and also more dignified things. But, like the rest, she cries that she'll do anything: scrub floors! For in the evocation of this ruin, in the very word *scrubbing*, there is something miserable which induces husbands' hearts to soften and lashes their self-esteem. In a hundred thousand homes all over the world, from Vladivostok to Vancouver, the same word bursts out, the same phrase resounds: "I'll go out and scrub floors, since this tramp has managed to destroy our home!"

Just like scrubbing floors, destroying a home creates an image. One has a vision of the red-and-black posters of the war, the exodus ("National Loan—Subscribe Now!"), the woman in a shawl pushing a broken-down baby carriage containing a screaming infant as she flees through a burning countryside. If women seem drawn by the image of the home destroyed, it's because in love they are what men are in business: they want to *build*. On this great vessel which bears us and which permits only the dead to land, the passengers' first preoccupation is to build something solid. The monument of the woman is the home. Before the hallucinating image of the home destroyed, how can the most hardened heart of man not feel a clutch of pity? The heart of woman too. The man weeps nervously, in hiccoughs; the woman, copiously. No amount of common sense will stem these floods of tears. The end of the scene has to be put off till the next day or even the next week. Life, even when it takes on the hues of classical drama, never includes unity of action.

That's why conjugal scenes are so different from what they become in the theater. The theater is said to be the mirror of life. But life is not a play. Transmitted over the footlights, life as one speaks it has a pathos impossible to accept on the stage. The theater is life reconsidered and corrected, condensed, laminated. The theater is a gigantic letting off of steam: on the part of the author, who makes his characters speak as he has never dared to speak himself; on the part of the actors, who play at the top of their voices roles they will never have the courage to assume in life; on the part of the spectators, who come to listen to what they do not wish to say, what they cannot say, in their own homes, and who find themselves sublimated in the skin of another. And everyone goes home contented and saying, "That's life!," when it's a quintessence of the life they do not live. (Of course, should a play happen to illustrate our own case before our eyes, and find by 11 P.M. a radical solution for it which strikes me as excellent, Thérèse instantly cries, "It's only a play!" Besides, she always recognizes everyone on the stage except herself.)

81

If only life had come to my aid! I often hoped, during the period of our drama, that life would help me. That's what the weaker vessels of my species hope for without admitting it: the solution which they won't have provoked themselves. I have so often been told not to do anything drastic. "Events always alter life in their own way." That's true, no doubt, but it would tend to prove that when there are no events, no life is possible. Without speaking of those bolts from the blue which so repeatedly occur in fiction or in the press—sudden heart attacks or airplane crashes—Thérèse might have fallen in love herself. Or gone mad. Time and again I heard her say at this time, "It's beginning to drive me mad." But no. Nothing. Nothing happened. Only in the theater does something ever happen, something known as the *coup de théâtre,* which precipitates the solution: suicide, angina pectoris, sudden withdrawal of the woman, who has understood at last and leaves the field clear.

Nothing like any of this happens in everyday life, which races on over every obstacle. The unforeseen never occurs. Never, above all, when one wants it to. If, by chance, a woman of forty disappears—this is the age at which one ought, as they say in America, to be able to turn her in for two twenty-year-olds—it's always someone adored by her husband. In the solid middle class, death reaps only in happy homes, at least when they have reached the age of having dramas. For proof of this, read the obituaries, always identical: "They never left each other. . . . One was

82

never seen without the other." As for the unhappy homes, they shouldn't rely on a stroke of fate to solve the crisis. Airplane accidents, the snapping of a funicular cable, incurable cancer, husbands who run over their wives when backing out of the garage, heart attacks in the bathtub— these are suppositions that the Devil sometimes slips into the minds of the martyred middle class, but, in practice, theatrical producers are the only ones to bring them off.*

Another principle: Life never helps you when you expect something of it. In spite of hideous scenes and a chronic state of pathological hysteria, in spite of the cries of "I feel as if I were going mad," "I think I'll die"—with the inevitable corollary of "Anyway, that would be the best thing for everybody, you'd all be rid of me"—Thérèse continues as solid as a rock.

One more principle: A woman never is going mad—at least not enough to have her put away—when she cries, "I think I'm going mad!" I heard that for months on end, and Thérèse never even went to consult a psychiatrist. Besides, there are no people like people who complain of always being ill for burying others. Despair kills only in fiction.

You must, therefore, take action yourself. Generally that's what you determine to do after meeting a friend in whom you've confided and whose advice has been "Better get it over with all at once. You're always afraid of going

---

* *Thérèse takes all her baths immediately after meals; it never does her any harm.*

the whole hog. What's the point of that? You don't want to kill her off by inches, do you? Well, then! Speak out frankly. You must operate coolly and calmly."

So here you are with your big butcher's knife, hacking, ripping, slashing away a whole section of the past which she believed intact and which was made moldy with lies. Everything collapses: past, present, future. Cries, tears, threats. And what do you see happen? A child awakening with a start, comes in pajamas in the nick of time to remind you that you have little ones. I collapse, you collapse, we collapse. We're back where we started.

You had picked a bad moment.

Another fundamental difference between fiction and reality. On the stage or screen, the moment the husband or wife selects to conclude the rupture always proves the perfect choice. That, no doubt, is why it's called the psychological moment. In life it is *never* the right moment. The proof is that I have already seized a dozen opportunities to speak, spread out over every month of the year, and each time Thérèse has said to me, "Really, you might have chosen a different time to throw this in my face. You always make a mess of everything you do!"

When it isn't "only a week before our anniversary," it's "just before we're going on vacation," or "That's a nice note to strike just as we're going home," or else "You're telling me all this only two weeks before Christmas? So you won't be seeing the New Year in with your children!" (Note the use of "your," which may become "my" or "our," depending on the way things develop.) To which are added the evenings before family reunions, first Communions, exams and those frustrating spring events, Mother's Day, and Father's Day, with their perpetual air of festivity, which completely prevent you from saying anything at all.

Anyway, it's too late; you have spoken.

Immediately after having "operated" (following the precepts of your friend who advocated getting it over with all at once), and while you're still reeling from the effect of the futile mess you've made, trembling, filled with remorse, torn by doubt, you meet the old childhood friend whom you had forgotten to consult, the trusty friend who has never let you down, and who, once brought abreast of the situation, unhesitatingly declared, "I have only one bit of advice to give you, old man: let life take its course. Don't provoke anything yourself—you may very well regret it someday, and regret it bitterly."

Here again, what a difference between life and the theater! In reality, and above all in the street, you never stop meeting people who advise you one way or another (never in the same way twice running): The man who thinks you should make a firm decision: "Better a good divorce than a bad marriage." The one who believes in a *modus vivendi:* "At all events, bear one thing in mind: From what I know of you, sensitive as you are, you'll never build a new happiness on the ruins of the old." The one who, on the other hand, feels that this double life is intolerable or threatens to become so sooner or later, and that anyway you haven't the right to stifle so rare a thing

85

as a Great Love. The one who makes a principle, in the same situation, of leaving both wife and mistress—for a while, at any rate: "You must take the plunge, old boy, take the plunge. It's painful, I know, but it's the only solution. Go away by yourself—you'll see things more objectively. When you come back, the situation will work itself out, you'll see."

If, like me, you're at all easily influenced, this becomes a nightmare.

Clearly, in the theater this type of nightmare can't exist. The author would never let his characters leave the stage to go down into the street and come under external influences, otherwise the progress of his play would be thwarted in the most provoking fashion.

Even if there weren't the counselors, whom you're at perfect liberty to avoid merely by not mentioning the problem to them, there would still be the whole world, all those people to whom you never speak but who nevertheless keep right on speaking to you. It's extraordinary, when you're on the verge of a rupture, the number of married couples you can pass in the street who look perfectly happy. You would almost think it was an air they adopted on purpose to annoy you.

Is the air of people in the street really their true one or something you simply attribute to them? When I go to a secret rendezvous, it seems to me that everyone I pass is fully aware of my turpitude and is looking at me as if I were going to commit a crime. They might almost have come out of a book of *leçons de chose,* object lessons: parents soberly out walking the baby; students weighed down with dictionaries, hurrying off to school; gentlemen setting out for their offices with briefcases under their arms, and so on. I would swear my path is strewn with industrious citizens who guess at my shady intentions. I have the impression of being cut off from life, honest life. My old middle-class depths rise up without my knowing it. I got the same sensation when, in the period of which I am writing, the children used to see me go off with furrowed brow, a heavy briefcase, an air of being in a hurry, for the office in the Rue de Châteaudun which was really Miriam's place in the Rue du Dobropol. As I shut the apartment door behind me, calling, "And behave yourselves, now," over my shoulder, I imagined I could hear, echoing up from the depths of the elevator shaft, the colossal guffaw of all the pure consciences hooting, "You're a fine one to talk, you old devil!"*

Whatever the part played by reality or autosuggestion in all this, I have never met so many people who lead simple lives as at the times when I have evolved a most complicated existence for myself. Nor have I ever met so many acquaintances who point out my good fortune to me: "Ah, my dear fellow, how I envy you! You have a

---

* I often notice the reverse phenomenon: When I go to the cinema intending to profit from the darkness to exchange a few kisses, I am surrounded by old ladies and children who, it seems, have their eyes glued on me. If I go there with Thérèse, we are generally seated behind a pair of lovers who nibble each other's necks the whole way through the film. And whenever, in hotels, I act the family man to the life, I am surrounded by illicit couples who flout me with the most ostentatiously unseemly behavior.

87

wife, children, a home, and excellent health on top of it all. You don't know how lucky you are."

People never know how lucky they are. But other people's luck never escapes them. They are there, happily, to keep you informed of it.

To all these considerations I should add that on the stage it is the simplest thing in the world to leave. Once the quarrel is over, he or she disappears through a door and the author doesn't give a fig what happens afterward, concerning himself not one iota with all the sordid little problems which rise up in normal life after the fatal words "You can pack your things and go!"—material problems (calculating the point of fall, financial arrangements, taking away small objects, moving out large ones, starting to pack, papers, division of property and so on) the settlement of which can take several months. And even now, when I have almost finished with this parallel between the theater and life, I've come nowhere near exhausting this most exhausting of the questions.

Besides, I myself have never reached the stage of packing my things. But I understand now why so many men prefer to give up and let themselves be swallowed body and soul by their homes, rather than be delivered alive to the fission of a double life. While setting aside any further comparison between life and the theater, I am mindful of the famous and much vaunted lure of forbidden fruit: "Without the spice of secrecy, love would be a drab affair. What makes it so fascinating is when it is forbidden."

I myself believed in this a little. I no longer believe in it at all. Take traveling, for instance. I have always found it exhausting to describe a trip on my return. But to describe without committing any errors a trip I haven't really made —this, though it may have been amusing once, is today beyond my strength. When I think that when I was hardly back from Le Lavandou I had to tell what the weather was like at Nancy and whether I had seen the Deplats—! And if only that had been all. But I had to do the following as well:

1. On leaving, feign boredom, complain of the tedium of having to leave home and go to Nancy, while stifling the joy I felt at being on my way to Le Lavandou. The superfine achievement being to contrive to provoke sympathy while simulating despair. ("How awful. Poor darling!") The superluxury of asking at the last minute, "Are you quite sure you don't want to come with me?"—a heroic method of proving you're going alone. For greater safety it's a good idea not to wait for a reply but to follow up this question with a sudden recollection: "Of course, I also have to stop off tomorrow night at Lunéville to see the Providence agent. What a nuisance!" The prospect of an evening at Lunéville with the Providence agent is such that it unfailingly casts a cold shower on any lurking feminine enthusiasm. Bar-le-Duc, Valenciennes, Lyons, Toul, Belfort, the north and the east in general and, out-

side France, Essen, Leeds and Birmingham, can be recommended as ideal stopping-off places for choking off any stray impulse to accompany you.

2. Make arrangements at Nancy with a reliable accomplice who would dispatch the telegram "SAFELY ARRIVED WISH YOU WERE WITH ME LOVE" and, if need be, forward any letters.

3. Provide myself, just before leaving Paris, with a box of preserved fruit from Nancy, together with picture postcards of the Place Stanislas, to find which at Le Lavandou might well have proved tricky.

4. Avoid spending too much time in the sun, which might give rise to "For someone who has just been to Nancy, you've acquired a remarkable tan." (It's not impossible to acquire a tan at Nancy, but even if this were true you would never be believed; once you start to lie, the truth itself becomes improbable.)

5. On leaving the hotel at Le Lavandou, take care to instruct them not to send a New Year's greeting card to my Paris address, which was entered in the hotel register ("With best wishes of the Hotel des Pins to its faithful clients").

6. Return to step 1 and operate in reverse: feign joy and relief at being able at last to sink back into the peace of the home, while smothering any trace of irritation or boredom.

I defy any normal man to play this game with serenity for more than a few months—let's say two years at the most. If you wish to play it for longer than that, you run the risk of finding it impossible to relax, either at home or anywhere else. To this rhythm my happiness soon frittered away.

And so I watched Miriam's youth running out through the hourglass of marriage—a marriage that wasn't hers. Within the cramped confines of that famous triangle in which the lack of imagination of Western legislators has enclosed us, asphyxia got the best of me: I went full circle and came back to my point of departure. Miriam and I: it was still that—and it was no longer that. For the first principle which I laid down with regard to the wife (What you give is nothing; what you take away is everything.) will also apply, after a certain length of time, to the mistress.

Ah, Miriam, beautiful child, sweet dove who had promised me you wouldn't destroy anything, would rise above everything, be content with what was reasonable—you too came to be haunted by the Spirit of Establishment, devoured by the sacred monster of Security.

One day, quite suddenly, she complained of the *Back Street* quality of her life. I wonder how women in her position used to voice their complaints before that film was made; the harm an American film producer may have done to as solidly established an institution as adultery is incalculable. Thereafter everything was stigmatized by those two words, *Back Street*, the symbol of disaster. From then on, Miriam's only preoccupation seemed to be with what she didn't have: dinner if I gave her lunch, the night if I devoted the afternoon to her, Sunday—ah, Sundays!—if I spent Saturday with her; and as for holidays—the school vacation of course.

For what, when all is said and done? To win that most fallacious of prizes and obtain what threatens to spoil everything: the daily round.

P.S.—No, Thérèse really has no cause to worry—I would be quite incapable of condensing all this into my answers, even if I wanted to. Besides, even if I reply that the French are often more faithful to their homes than to their wives, and that wives should show a little indulgence over their husbands' foibles, that will hardly compromise me.

5

THE CHILDREN

1. How many children do you have?
2. What is the average number of children per French household (fathers 30 to 50 years of age)?
3. Do your children take after you?
4. Do they cause you anxiety?
5. What, in your opinion, is the distinctive characteristic of today's youth?
6. . . . . .

No DOUBT the world contains children who choose their friends wisely, in such a way that they come home feeling happy and fully conscious of the efforts their parents are making to insure them a decent and pleasant life. At least, I like to think this must be so. But there are also others, like mine, who pick their friends in such a way that they come home resentful, with a feeling of being worse off than anyone else and, as the Americans say, frustrated.

Fantastic. My children must surely now and then meet young people who have *less*. But the "other" children about whom they talk until I'm sick and tired of it always have *more*. I only have to buy my son a bicycle for him to become, the very next day, the best friend of a boy who has a scooter. And if I let my daughter go once a week to the cinema, she immediately rattles off the names of three friends who can go whenever they like, which is to say all the time.

I was thinking about this just now on the beach. Last summer the children plagued me ceaselessly over the advantages of an orange inflatable dinghy which our neighbors had and which they found an object of irresistible attraction. "Oh, Papa, you must buy one! It would be terrific!" The way they went on, once they owned one their wildest dreams would have come true; it was the only thing in the world they really wanted.

"We'll see about it next year," I would say, "if you behave yourselves."

I wound up envying the father who had bought his children the beach's orange dinghy, the cynosure of all the summer people. I began to develop ideas of becoming this universally coveted Father, a longing to be able in turn to say, "If your children would like to try it, by all means let them go right ahead. Robert and Brigitte will be delighted to take them out in it. But of course—I absolutely insist!" And my children would be happy. And they would make other people's children happy.

And, above all, I would be left in peace.

Well, I did it. I committed this act of folly. I bought the orange boat—the same model as the one that had filled my children's dreams. The three of us, on this beach where we have come to spend our vacation (not the same one as last year, for I would have found it embarrassing to meet the man with the orange dinghy; here I stood a good chance of being the only man to have one—and I am!), blew the thing up gleefully, nay, inflated it with our joy. Never had an air chamber been the channel for so much buoyancy of spirit. For a brief time, while we were blowing it up, I had the sensation of being the ideal father who knows how to fulfill the aspirations of his children—the father fulfilled, the fulfilling father, the father-friend, the sports-model paterfamilias.*

While we launched the boat, this sensation continued. It lasted for precisely two hours. Precisely until the moment when the young Favre-Liberts (the canned-food people, worth millions) passed us in a spray of foam from their outboard motor, giving us the friendly wave of people delighted to see you capsize in their wash. The dazzling passage of this frothing arrow was enough for my children to find it absolutely out of date to have to row. By the time we got back to the beach their eyes were popping out with envy of the mahogany meteor of the Favre-Liberts, to whom the paternal sardines dispensed every kind of nautical luxury. To heap Pelion on Ossa, they made the acquaintance of some other young people with a Chris-Craft. And I was left alone on the beach with damned inflatable

---

* A dream harder to achieve than you would imagine. One day, after a dispute, I tried to reason with my son by saying to him, "After all, Robert, you'd like me to be your pal, wouldn't you?" "Pal? Pal?" he replied after a moment's reflection. "Do you suppose I would ever think of having a pal of your age, Papa?"

dinghy, while the children were invited on board a back-firing racer.

Obviously this vessel which they so avidly desired when · they didn't have one is completely out of date this year. As a last resort it might be acceptable if it had a motor attached to it, but then again . . . It would be better, they say, to trade it in for an Albatross, a Riva or some Phantom I-don't-know-what (*they* know: Phantom IV). I too would enjoy myself much more. With this one you can't do anything, especially not ski, when the only amusing thing to do is water-ski—like the Favre-Liberts or the Tchernaïans.

"You'll see, Papa, it's super!"

Meanwhile I did my utmost, by means of long, solitary outings, to demonstrate to them the sporting virtues of rowing and the tranquil benefits of the inflatable dinghy. Despite my repugnance, they insisted on taking me in tow, tethered to the Favre-Liberts' meteor by a rope. My face when I capsized was apparently a scream (pardon—*terrific*). No doubt it was, but I preferred to return to my peaceful exercises. Even so, in the midst of this gilded youth cleaving the waves trailing nymphs and Apollos at forty miles an hour, what sort of figure can I have cut in my rubber bathtub?

Only yesterday they again returned to the charge: "Oh, Papa, you absolutely *must* buy an Albatross—it's sensational! Please, Papa, buy one?"

As if I could sink a million francs (even old ones) in a boat!

"You know perfectly well," said Thérèse, "that your father isn't able to." To hear Thérèse, one would swear she was referring to some physical incapacity. She doesn't yearn for an Onassis, of course, but you get the feeling she had hoped for something better.

And what then? Suppose I bought an Albatross? I'm willing to bet that at the end of a week the children would discover intimate friends who had the supermodel.

I try to resist: "You're insatiable! You're never contented with what you have. When I was your age . . ."

I hardly dare write those last five words. I can still hear my children's caustic comments: "When you were our age, when you were our age. You're always saying that, Papa." And yet it's true: In my young days children were more reasonable, their parents had greater authority, life was easier, people had better manners, fabrics were stronger, the franc was more stable, the country had a healthier outlook. True, no doubt, but that's exactly what my father used to tell me, and probably my son will say the same things to his children. In this land of prosperity, people never stop swearing that previous times were better.

"Your little friends are lucky," I say bitterly, "to have rich fathers!"

However stupid this glimpse of the obvious may sound, it isn't always confirmed. Very often my son remarks to me, "Oh no, Papa. Xavier has a car, and his father doesn't have a sou. They just manage somehow."

It seems that nowadays there are a great many people who barely earn enough to live on, yet they find the means to pay for scooters, tape recorders and other luxuries for their children.

The luxuries rain down on them from heaven before they even have the bare necessities. And nobody is surprised at it except men like me who, having learned from the tenderest age not to put the cart before the horse, think carefully before they spend the smallest sum. A case of middle-class atavism which I doubtless owe to my mother, who always said, when it was a question of buying something, "I'll see about it. I'll think it over," and generally didn't buy it. She died thinking it over.

Are these the same times? Are these the same people? To me, everything seems changed. In the summer, for instance, I see a mass of young people living on yachts or estates of which they could never possibly be the owners. They're simply young, good-looking and from families that are fairly well off. The rest follows naturally: they are invited, perpetually invited. The other day, while I was gazing through my binoculars at the *Rakaju*, a white yacht anchored in the bay, I noticed one of these blond Adonises nonchalantly stretched out on a blue mattress. He never left his mat except to help himself to a whiskey or else offer one to some new arrival. Judging from the detachment with which this young prince, reclining at his ease in a short-sleeved black silk shirt and blue linen slacks, was doing the honors of the ship and emptying its stores, one would have sworn he was the owner or at least the owner's heir.

"No," my son informed me. "That's Alec Dewitt—just

98

a friend of the Favre-Liberts. He's spending his vacation on the yacht."

I admire this detachment, this nonchalance—"You know me, anything suits me."—of these young men who, without spending a penny, plow the ocean wave on board yachts just good enough to receive them. For my part, I would be a little embarrassed. They aren't at all. I can only conclude that there are some people who never feel really at home except when staying with other people. The mountebanks of our day, minstrels of modern courts, beguilers of bored nabobs, they must bring their millionaire hosts that spark of bohemianism and wit which they lack. Stillborn writers, bogus artists, interior decorators, champions of surf riding and the Hula Hoop, surrealists of every hue, they are the Vacation Kings. They alone can lord it on the bridge, absorbed in emptying bottles of old Scotch and ogling the naiads on board, while the owner fights with his crew and develops ulcers trying to find out whether he'll be able to take on fresh fuel at Palma.

"Do your children take after you?"
Right now, my children follow only the Favre-Liberts. In vain I tell them we come from different worlds (their new friends are at the Carlton, we at the Hotel de la Plage), that by mixing with these people they're going to acquire a taste for luxury and comfort which I'm not in a position to satisfy. The effect is nil. I hear nothing but "Patrice Favre-Libert told me . . . ," "The Favre-Liberts think . . ."

I'll just have to accept the fact: my children prefer the promptings of any outsider to those of their parents. True, only strangers seem to appreciate their qualities. Barely have I finished bewailing the laziness, lack of conscience and offhandedness of my children when the very next stranger I meet announces, "You have such delightful children! And so well brought up!"

When the stranger is famous, it becomes delirium.

Not so very long ago—since it happens every three or four months—I found that my daughter's room was harboring one stranger more. I say "stranger" because he gained her intimacy without ever being introduced to me. Nor to her, for that matter. But this stranger is more famous than I shall ever be. As it happens, he is the son of an Oriental potentate whom my daughter, like everyone else, calls by his first name, Vaduz. "He's marvelous—don't you think so, Papa?" On the walls of her room he has joined the color photographs of all the princes my daughter has had a crush on during the past year or two, following the dictates of fashion. Demigods beside whom I count for very little. There is an American actor, an Austrian skiing champion, a member of the British royal family, a French dress designer, and so on. At the moment, then, it is Vaduz.

This young man, who a fortnight ago never even existed, so to speak, and whose name I had never even heard of, seems to have become the number one preoccupation of my daughter and of forty million French men and women. They know where he dined last night, where he's going to sleep tomorrow and almost with whom, what he likes best for breakfast, the make of ski he prefers, the number of cars he has, his favorite actresses, and so on. At least my daughter knows all these things, and I have to know them too unless I want her to look on me as an ignoramus.

For all this, there's nothing to compare with the newspapers in general and the weeklies in particular. I have to admit, without them no fame is assured; but for them it's impossible to know every detail of the private lives of princes. The weekly magazine, gossip and the cinema have become the teats that suckle our youth. (That makes three, I agree, but aren't our young people monsters?) The front cover of *Paris-Match* or *Elle* weighs more heavily in the destiny of a young girl than the baccalaureate and teaching examinations combined. "She made the cover of *Paris-Match*" my daughter and her friends will tell each other, just as I might have cried in the old days, "She won first place in the interschool General Contest!"

Once a face has been engraved on the memories of ten or twelve million people, how does it remain famous? Nowadays celebrity nurtures itself in only a very small way on what gave rise to it in the first place, whether film, novel or play. Suppose a man achieves fame through his painting. It is by no means through his painting that his promoter will cultivate his notoriety. But should he confide to a newspaperman that the master can paint only between midnight and 6 A.M. while devouring sugared almonds in front of a skull, that's news and will get him talked about far more than a long article on his art. Celebrity is a plant which has to be watered with anecdotes.

And so my children are growing up in the anecdotal cult of ephemeral divinities. Thanks to the gossip columns and the magazines, they end up knowing far more about some star or prince than they do about me. The newspapers will be the death of me. I haven't the time to read the really important parts. Doubtless this is a mistake. Very often the stories they tell are so many examples provided as pasture for my children's imaginations to graze in. Barely is a new film star born when they reveal that she's a girl with an excellent background. Like ours. Whose father is a middle-class man of principle. Like me. Who had tried every means in his power to prevent his daughter from becoming a film actress. As I would. But his daughter rebelled, ran away and made her own career. Today has brought fame and, of course, a reconciliation with her family. How could such examples fail to influence my daughter? The cinema is an Omnipotent Force beside which paternal authority counts for nothing. You can spend fifteen years of your life in making of your child a well-balanced sensitive being with a feeling for right and wrong; in one hour, a film will alienate her completely. One of those films, naturally, in which a ridiculed, slandered, insulted middle class is made to appear Social Enemy Number One; films in which it is shown that raising a family is the sheerest lunacy and that paying back borrowed money is the most old-fashioned of obligations.

I sometimes wonder what young people would do if they had no elders to shock. Elders? Well, let's use the term—

always the same one—*middle class*. Poor abused middle classes, which have no worse detractors than their own children, unless it be the middle classes themselves! If you didn't exist, they would have to invent you. For if there were no middle class to transfix, against which or what would this need to shock, with which the young seem to be obsessed, be directed? In a world without a middle class, they would die of boredom. The cigarette which the schoolboy clumsily smokes in the street he smokes less for his own pleasure than in defiance of the middle class in general and his middle-class father in particular. I was reading the other day that a gang of youths in jeans and sweatshirts had invaded the paddock at the Deauville race track and then, to the outrage of the regular frequenters of such elegant spots, had installed themselves in the grandstand with that indifference and offhandedness which are the attributes of youth. It's more than probable that, had the regulation dress for the paddock at Deauville been sweatshirts and jeans, these young men would have put on top hats and morning coats. In just the same way, if her grandmother had been in the habit of driving her car without shoes, a young actress renowned for driving about barefoot would find it *divine* to press the accelerator with a shoe. In a world in which violence, delinquency, negligence of dress (is it dirt that makes the delinquent or the delinquent who breeds the dirt?) and the art of treating love as a piece of futility were the attributes of the middle class, who knows if these young hooligans wouldn't reinvent good manners, modesty and romanticism?

103

Who knows even whether if they lived in a world in which disillusionment was general, they wouldn't decide to give up wearing an air of boredom when they're enjoying themselves? Sometimes, just as I'm about to cross the threshold of my home, harsh gusts of hysterical music reach me through the door. I open it to find myself confronted by ten young couples who stare at me as if I were a sort of prehistoric gate crasher with such supercilious amazement that I almost feel like apologizing for entering my own apartment. While I stand speechless in the doorway, barely recognizing two or three familiar faces (those of my children) amidst this hirsute fauna and trying to visualize my chaotic apartment as it had been when I left it to go to the office, I feel the young wolves' eyes boring into me like a century gauge and hurry as fast as I can to my room after dropping a "Don't get up on my account" —a waste of time, anyway, since nobody has budged. I had forgotten my daughter was having a party.

Bah! It's their age. I have nothing much to say against it, only I would so like to see them enjoying themselves. They look as if they were doing anything but that. The cha-cha-cha, the Charleston and rock 'n' roll are gay, spirited, vital dances. And yet, judging by the supremely disgusted air these young men adopt as they spin their partners around, flinging them about as if they were pulling off their shirts, one is entitled to wonder whether they're enjoying themselves to the point of boredom or whether they're really bored by enjoying themselves. They must cut exactly the same figure at an examination or a funeral—though I would readily suspect them of improving these occasions by shrieking with laughter, obsessed as they are by a need to do exactly the opposite of what is normally done. Perhaps they'll begin to laugh at fifty?

In the meantime, their expression, I have no doubt, is the one it's the thing to have: that air of having seen and done everything before they have even embarked on life.

ANSWER CARD NO. 5

QUESTION NO. 1 . . . 2 . . . .

QUESTION NO. 2 . . . 2:3 . . . . . .

QUESTION NO. 3 *Not much* . .

QUESTION NO. 4 . *Yes* . . . .

QUESTION NO. 5 *Boorishness* . .

QUESTION NO. 6 *A blasé air* . .

NAME AND ADDRESS OF SENDER

P. Blot
10 Rue de Turnville Paris

GREAT CONTEST

FOR THE

AVERAGE FRENCHMAN

17 AVENUE MONGHTURZ

PARIS 2

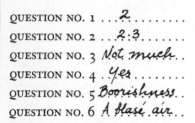

6

OTHER PEOPLE

1. Do others have an important influence on your behavior?
2. Do you consider yourself superior, equal or inferior to your average fellow man?
3. What are the good points and the shortcomings that you find in others and that . . .

No DOUBT I am influenced by Thérèse, who never ceases to hold my friends and relations up as an example to me, but I have to admit it: people as a whole always seem to know more about things than I do. I've just confirmed this fact once again in the train. In my compartment, which certainly was going no less fast than the rest—about seventy miles an hour—there was a gentleman who could distinguish clover from alfalfa, wheat from oats, apple trees from plum trees, crows from rooks, larches from spruces. At one moment, speaking of rock formation, he even went so far as to give us a dissertation on the Jurassic, if it wasn't the Cretaceous.

But enough. Such travelers may be rather exhausting in the long run, but how superior they are to me, who, outside my own job, can't even call things by their proper names but merely see fields, trees, greenery and birds without being able to give any of them their specific labels. When I think that, after having clung to life on this earth for nearly half a century, I could die tomorrow without being able to describe in accurate detail the design of a thousand-franc note or the wording on a ticket for the Métro, I feel dizzy, dizzy with a sense of my own shortcomings. That's why I feel such admiration for those who at a mere glance can distinguish a hawk from a pigeon through the window of an express.

It was thus that the gentleman of the Cretaceous period appeared to me, as he described the countryside to the child sitting on his knee. He wasn't the only one of his species. Another traveler, after having given the number of inhabitants of Poitiers to almost the nearest dozen, which already wasn't bad, next expounded with mathematical precision the position of North African manpower in France. A third, munching an apple, revealed that this fruit, rich in vitamin B and phosphates, soothes the nerves and helps you to sleep well. The conversation then passed to food in general, and I learned that of all fish the whiting is the richest in potassium, while the cod wins the day as regards nitrogen.

I was astounded. And—mark this well—it was a train taken at random; naturally it was going to Montauban like myself, but that was the only reason I had chosen it.

While busy pretending to read my newspaper, I couldn't help reflecting on all the elementary knowledge in which I was lacking. One example: the points of the compass. It's staggering how many people there are on the beaches in summer who can tell you in a twinkling whether the wind is south southeast or north northwest. Well, shall I confess it? At forty-five, I am quite incapable of saying with any certainty at any point on the globe, where the sun rises or sets. East? West? Once a year, generally during the summer vacation, someone informs me—and then I forget.

While I was brooding somewhat anxiously on the extent of my shortcomings, the train stopped at the station of X. There now came to fill an empty seat in our compartment a lady of a certain age, as they say of those who are nearer eighty than eight, well-to-do in appearance, with a little pigskin traveling bag. She was one of those females who love to be reassured. Judging from the number of travelers who want to be reassured in trains, whether about their connections ("Will I make my connection at Limoges, do you think, monsieur?"), the amount of time they have in which to get a sandwich in the station buffet, which car their luggage is in, drafts, whether it's better to travel facing or back to the engine, or even the actual direction of the train, I end up wondering if only beings suffering from pathological anxiety ever travel, just as one wonders if only people with coughs ever go to the theater. Take the problem of smoke. There's nothing like a train to help you find people who announce that they're irritated by smoke. There's smoke everywhere—in the streets, in houses, in night clubs, in restaurants, in any public place. But does anyone ever complain of smoke in a living room and ask you to stop? No. On the other hand, you have only to get into a train to meet hypersensitive beings whom the faintest wisp of cigarette smoke threatens with death.

Our lady traveler, for one, was a particular sort of anxiety type: she suffered from the dining-car neurosis. (A certain number of travelers like this are racked by a desire to eat from 4 P.M. onward because they have just learned that there isn't a dining car.) Three people reassured her. One must suppose, however, that she drew no comfort from this, since when the conductor (whose chief task is to confirm to the neurotic what they already know) passed by she asked him all over again, as if in need of an official guarantee, "There *is* a dining car, isn't there?" A question hardly calculated to please those who had already informed her. "Because it's most important I should know," she explained, as if to excuse herself.

There was a pause. Then, calling on one fellow traveler in particular as a witness, but addressing the compartment in general, the lady volunteered, "It's very important for me because I'm on an extremely strict diet. You see, I have a very small liver. Just imagine, it stopped growing when I was only nine! The intestine, on the other hand . . ." At this moment she suddenly turned to me. "You, monsieur, for example, do you have twelve yards like everyone else?"

I remained speechless, as if I didn't know her language. Happily replying for me, she went on. "Of course you have! Well, I have eighteen! You can picture the work they have to do! I'm obliged to eat crackers and vegetables in small quantities every three hours."

Whereupon, pursuing her monologue, the lady informed us that she had undergone a lengthy treatment in Switzerland, in a model clinic such as exists only in Switzerland.

"Whatever people say, the Swiss are pretty good at that sort of thing. I've always told my daughter that. 'If you have to have a baby someday, go to Switzerland,' I tell her. 'It's incomparably better than anywhere else. So clean!' Ah, they could teach us a thing or two."

Apart from depriving me of any desire to visit the dining car, the lady's eighteen yards had made a vivid impression on me. Perhaps not so much her eighteen as my own twelve. The fact of knowing that I carried this long yardage wobbling about inside me moved me as deeply as if I had been told I contained a boa constrictor. Another one of those things everyone has known since he went to school and which I've forgotten. Infuriating!

Oh, how much people know about everything! And how well they know how to impart their knowledge to the first comer. I too know about some things—things of which possibly these travelers were quite ignorant. I could have told them about our electric robot which does seventy-five thousand multiplications a minute. But I can't talk glibly like other people. To begin with, I always miss the opportunity to start talking. By the time I've made up my mind to begin, it's too late.

Is this simply due to shyness? I'll soon grow to believe it. To end up believing something, all you have to do is begin. If I'm so dim, so reserved, it's perhaps simply because, unlike these others, I don't know how to do my act and don't feel an imperious need to proclaim the things I know, the things I've done. Like the way we were treated, in that memorable compartment, to an exposition on Australian sheep. By examining with an absorbed air some sample sheepskins which he had extracted from his suitcase (prodigious, the number of things people manage to extract from their baggage to attract attention), one of my heroes had managed to get himself questioned about his activities. We were accordingly informed that he went to buy sheepskins in Australia for the town of Mazamet, which was endowed with the best water in the world for curing them. Examination of these sheepskins between Limoges and Brive was quite uncalled for. This gentleman, it was plain to see, knew his skins by heart. He wouldn't learn anything more from them during the train ride. But they would arouse curiosity: he could talk, do his act of counting sheep.

The gentleman of the Cretaceous age, doubtless having no intention of being left out, succeeded through the tobacco trick in letting us know he had been in Madagascar. "You see," he told the child, pursuing his botany course, "that's tobacco. You know, when I came back from Madagascar . . ." Children often act as catalysts for the performances of the grownups. How many fathers on vaca-

114

tion, before playing with their children, first make sure that everyone is watching and wait before saying something to their offspring until there is someone within earshot?

Who, in fact, doesn't have his act? On our last organized tour of Italy, we found ourselves one evening in a restaurant in Genoa. About a dozen French sailors, whose cruiser had put into the port, sat themselves down at a nearby table. Of all the acts in the world, that of sailors on leave is one of the most characteristic:

1. A period of relative calm during which our sailors allow all Italians, French, Americans and other foreigners present enough time to observe them. Correct behavior. The prestige of France comes first.

2. Beginning of the act. The waitress is summoned. First, what is her name? "Celerina! Say, that's a pretty name, Celerina." From now on, they begin to play sailors on a spree. They may well have felt no particular inclination to do so (there are always two or three timid ones), but, for the renown of their country and the fleet, there are certain imperatives: one must remain true to the stereotyped image of the lusty sailor who ribs the waitresses, drinks hard and sings bawdy songs. We were treated that evening to the complete act down to the inevitable fisticuffs which split the table into two camps, the scene over the bill, one of them carried out dead drunk and the intervention of the police.

I'll end up by believing that, three or four hundred

years after his first appearance on earth, man, whether sailor or traveling salesman, finds nothing harder than being natural.

The train is the touring theater of the citizen-players. But it's at lunchtime that other people impress me most.

Wouldn't everyone like to meet the most balanced man in the world, who never makes a mistake, knows everything, explains everything and is a model of conscientiousness, farsightedness, simplicity, modesty, boldness, subtlety and common sense? I'm in a position to reveal that this man exists. I can even indicate where and when he's to be seen: between 1 P.M. and 3 P.M. in every restaurant in France (and at night between 8 P.M. and 1 A.M. in millions of homes). For this phenomenal man has the gift of ubiquity.

At lunch the world appears to me to be peopled with wonderfully balanced people with unimpeachable morals, an infallible soundness of judgment, a luminous intelligence, complete objectivity, an inventive genius permanently on the alert, and absolute loyalty—who live surrounded by imbeciles, lunatics, careerists, dupes, megalomaniacs, loafers, cadgers, gangsters and incompetents, and who spend their time curbing the appetites of some, putting others back on the right road, helping these to benefit from their ideas, thwarting the Machiavellian schemes of those, narrowly avoiding catastrophes, re-establishing order everywhere and saying the right thing at the right moment. For these geniuses of the lunch table, born between noon

116

and 2 P.M., know at once how to find the missing ingredi-
ent, the perfect retort, the right man for the job. You wonder what would become of the world if they weren't there
to make it go round. They have a monopoly of that famous product of Gaul, sound common sense. In short,
they're "good men."

On behalf of my company, I sometimes happen to take
part in so-called "business lunches." If I'm to believe my
companions, like those seated at the neighboring tables,
I'm surrounded by geniuses. To hear them—"I set my engineers to work on it," or, better still, "I got my directors
together and told them . . ."—you would swear they were
superchiefs of superconcerns. When I refer to my director,
it's clear that he is placed above me, whereas these supermen seem to have a swarm of directors at their feet. Truth
to tell, I sometimes wonder, particularly at lunch, if France
isn't uniquely populated by presidents and directors general. But I'll leave the talking to these magnates.

On my left, that day, I had Lucidity. "This morning,"
the fellow was saying, "I saw my heads of departments.
They seemed in a terrible state. 'What's the matter, gentlemen?' I asked them. 'Is something bothering you?' Do you
know what it was? They couldn't understand how they
were going to use two-twenty-two with tubulures of sixty.
There they were, stumped, completely lost. I had to burst
out laughing. 'Come, come,' I said, 'that's not so very
serious, after all. You're drowning yourself in a puddle—
and a pretty small one at that. Just stop and think for a
moment. What does it really amount to? Here you have

117

some two-twenty-two, and there you have tubulures of sixty. And what do you suppose the one-six reinforcements are for, eh?' Now, really, it makes sense doesn't it? It was crystal clear. But no, they were at their wits' end. That was the one thing they hadn't thought of. They make me laugh. There they were, fumbling around, racking their brains, and the answer was staring them in the face, but they couldn't see it. You can't imagine the time I can waste with trivialities of this type. You'd never guess! It's quite simple: I spend my whole time at it!"

How could I have failed to evince the greatest admiration for this man? And yet he had hardly fallen silent when the same genius of lucidity reappeared, this time at the table on my right, bald and decorated:

"I had warned them six months ago. When they came to ask my advice, I made myself perfectly clear. 'With the cost price you've got there,' I told them, 'you'll never break even.' 'We shall see,' they replied. 'I've seen enough already to suit me,' I told them. 'Go on and try it if you're so anxious. We'll discuss it again in three months' time.' I knew exactly what would happen—no need to be a prophet to tell that—but they were determined not to listen. The result? Today they come sniveling to me and weep on my shoulder. They beg me to take the thing over. Think of it! As if I didn't have anything better to do! Thanks a lot. Let them get out of their own mess, since they thought so much of themselves. It's not my responsibility. And if I did help them would they listen to me

118

afterward? Not on your life. And for all the gratitude they'd show me . . . Ah, gratitude, we all know about that. Anyway, the irresponsibility of these people! Complete lack of common sense, the most basic, el-e-men-ta-ry common sense."

Is it possible that there could be men so stupid as not to have listened in time to this expert's judicious advice? Reason, Clear-sightedness, Common Sense, he was all of these and he had been preaching in the wilderness. How can anyone let such an opportunity pass with impunity? It makes me shudder.

It was clear, at any rate, that I had fallen among a den of geniuses. How many of them were there to the square yard? Two would already have struck me as a lot, when yet a third made me strain my ears to my left. This time it was Generosity.

"As anyone will tell you, it was I who got Chalut's foot on the ladder for him. It was I who got him into Toureau's. I who brought him his first customers. I who helped him to get started by advancing him the cash he needed to set up on his own. In 'fifty-six, if I hadn't been there, he'd have lost his shirt. And today he comes to touch me for five hundred thousand. Frankly, I said 'Nothing doing!' Mind you, it wasn't because of the actual money—what's five thousand new francs more or less? No, it was the principle of the thing."

You can feel it in your bones: this man is generous. But no sucker. He didn't refuse to lend five thousand new francs out of perverseness. His heart urged him to do it, but reason said no. He obeyed a principle. He was speaking as a self-made man:

"I built up my own business from nothing. I started right from scratch. Began with a mere two hundred twenty-five thousand francs' worth of savings, what do you think of that? Started off with a workshop, a milling machine and two lathes. O.K. Today I have three factories and seven hundred men working for me! If I make a gross profit of four thousand million a year,* what do I owe it to? Quite simply, hard work and what little I have up here"—tapping his forehead with his finger. "And now they'd like me to merge with them by making a so-called holding company. Do you know what I replied? 'Gentlemen,' I told them, 'I'd starve before I'd accept any offer of yours. I'd rather continue on my own little line.'"

From this evidence, subversive powers were trying to encircle this pure conscience and force him to be swallowed up by one of the great trusts. But his common sense held firm. He wouldn't let himself be put upon: he would continue on his own little line, his modest little branch line bordered on each side by factories and cottages all belonging to him, the fruits of his own humble genius, his own gumption, and at the end of it he would find, come rain come shine, his own little millions.

But where are the others, then? Where are the ones who drown in puddles, who can see no farther than their own

* *Old francs.*

noses, who make a hash of things, who shirk responsibilities? Where are those who understand nothing about anything, those who have fallen flat on their faces, who are too long in the tooth, too short of sight, too woolly-minded —and empty bellied? Where are those who never know the score, where are the rudely awakened, where are the bunglers, the crackbrained and the dupes? If there are so many who put the cart before the horse, always arrive late, believe in nothing or swallow everything, fly too high or have too much lead in their boots, they must be somewhere.

But where?

Simply in other restaurants, or else at home, busy telling their friends or their wives the same stories—the other way around. There they are: those who have made a complete mess of things describing how they left the others gaping open-mouthed; those who were drowning in puddles proving themselves the best swimmers in the world; those who couldn't see beyond the ends of their own noses revealing themselves to be hyper-clear-sighted; those who were soft asserting that they were the only ones to show any guts.

That is how you can spend a whole day in this world of imbeciles without ever setting eyes on even an embryonic idiot. You must admit it's stupid.

7
HONORS

~~~~~~

1. Do you like honors?
2. Have you been decorated?
3. If not, would you like to be?
4. For what?
5. Of all the decorations, which would you like
   most to have?

~~~~~~

I CAN'T SAY I have a thirst for honors. This is not, however, for want of celebrating them punctiliously at those banquets during which the executives and the staff of our company—a huge basketful of lobsters—learn that, from the humblest porter to the president-director general, they're just One Big Family. (There is a grain of truth in this, at least if one considers the family as a hotbed of discord.)

The other night it was Tissayre's turn. Wishing to extol the merits of this director, famous for his severity, selfishness, servility, soft-soapery and savage lust for power, M. de Stumpf-Quichelier fell back on the ritual formula, "Under

123

what appears at times to be a rough exterior, our friend conceals a heart of gold."

Although it may be quite normal, when one has such a heart, to conceal it with the utmost care, I have never liked this type of reticence. Have a normal heart and no one ever mentions it. Conceal it for forty years and it is revealed amidst great pomp and has the Legion of Honor hung on it.

Once again I heard our president, upholding the virtues of Teamwork, proclaim to the world that our company is not one of those inhuman concerns in which men, reduced to the status of ciphers, work obscurely at issues in which they have no share. No! "It is my company as it is yours; it is ours." My-yours-his, ours-yours-theirs. These love feasts evoke for me those end-of-term school dinners where teachers, proctors and students observed an uneasy truce under the melting gaze of the principal and the assistant principal. Always this feeling of having remained at school ever since I left it: the adjutant general took the place of the chief proctor, the head of my department that of the adjutant general, the director that of the head of my department, the Legion of Honor that of the Prize for Excellence. At fifty-five I'll be graded by my superiors.

Once again we endured the avalanche of epithets and classic formulas: Never was a decoration more highly deserved (the others were apparently not so very highly deserved); if there was anything which could cause surprise, it was that this excellent fellow hadn't received it before; he was to be congratulated from the bottom of our hearts;

the honor, of which no one was more worthy than its new-est recipient, would reflect its glory on the whole com-pany; we were gathered there to pay tribute not only to the devoted colleague and tireless worker, but also to the Friend, a true friend who had never faltered when times were hard, who had stood by us through thick and thin. Worn-out clichés which appear brand-new to their bene-ficiary, as if he were the first to reap them. Man is a strange animal who never thinks it's cancer when he has it and who suffers from the Legion of Honor when he doesn't have it.

This shower of platitudes fell gently on the head of Tissayre, who sat there blushing scarlet and moist of eye. In himself he had at last found someone over whom to grow maudlin. Soon it was his turn to speak. An exchange of clichés: Didn't feel worthy of such an honor; was moved and touched beyond all words; would remember this day as the finest of his life; was well aware that it wasn't he alone who was thus being honored but, through him, all those with whom he had worked and would continue to work hand in hand; finally, owed it to himself to associate with this tribute, of which he felt most undeserving, the one who for over thirty years had devotedly proved herself at once wife, friend and wisest of counselors.

Mme. Tissayre, at the center of the table of honor, wiped away a fat tear with the corner of a delicately poised hand-kerchief. This public consecration of her marriage in the presence of Tissayre's secretary, Mlle. Dréville (sitting at the end of the table), whose intimate connections with him were common knowledge, poured an incomparable balm over her heart. Tissayre might well see his secretary every day between six and eight; this speech, by affirming the legitimacy of his wife's claims before two hundred and fifty people, cast Mlle. Dréville back into the shadows for eternity. Ten years of conjugal misery shriveled up in the warm sunshine of the Legion of Honor.

Soon came the solemn moment.

"I now make way," said the chief, "for the Undersecretary of State for Commerce, who has been generous enough to honor this gathering with his presence."

I don't know how the management does it, but every time there's a Legion of Honor to be pinned to someone's breast it finds a retired Cabinet minister or a practicing undersecretary of state, or at the very least a bureau chief who happens to be free that evening and makes one of those set speeches designed for the festivities of big business in which only the names of the firm and the recipient of the honor have to be altered. When I think that year in and year out, sometimes as often as two or three times a week, on the dot of 11:30 P.M. these politicians embrace about a hundred men whom they do not know, it takes away any faint desire I may still have to become a minister.

The Undersecretary of State for Commerce rose and began to speak. He did it as no one else had yet done it that evening. You saw immediately the difference between the amateurs and the professional. He was one of those adepts at circumlocution whose text you're tempted to send to the laundry to see what would be left of it after.

126

There are, in fact, two types of speechmaking politician: the long-distance truck driver who knows to perfection how to describe the roads beset with bumps and potholes in which the vehicle of state risks coming to grief, and the navigator. The Undersecretary of State was an amphibian, with a marked predilection for a maritime vocabulary, which is a capital thing to possess if you wish to make a good orator. The captain standing fast at the helm, the pilot skilled at avoiding reefs, at riding the storm, at rounding tempestuous capes, the vessel brought safely to its haven—it was all there, rolled out in long phrases abruptly broken off without being properly completed. With orators the principle of Suspense consists in fact in never ending one sentence without having embarked on the following one: "Having thus examined every aspect of the problem, I would like now to pass on, but I must first add that—" A normal man would have come to the end, period. A politician, having come to the end, hastens to add—at least, he is about to add—but he abruptly stops. That is Suspense. The Undersecretary of State was a veritable maniac in this respect. He gave proof of it right from the start:

"We are all gathered here this evening to celebrate, in the person of one man, the glory of a great company, your company, which has ever been not only at the forefront of progress in the sphere* of professional life, but also a model of energetic and forceful expansion—and I would like to specify . . ."

---

* A good orator always finds a way to fit in a sphere somewhere or other.

127

The speaker took at least sixty seconds to call to mind what he was going to specify—which still remained pretty vague. Then, as soon as he could, he dropped the subject of Tissayre, about which he knew very little, to emphasize the vital role our company was playing in the move toward economic recovery which was beginning to appear on the horizon and which would beyond doubt become increasingly prominent "once the cape of autumn has been rounded—for I can tell you all . . ."

Finally the sacramental phrase: "In the name of the President of the Republic and by virtue of the powers which are invested in me, I now appoint you Chevalier of the Legion of Honor."

Ah, this Legion of Honor!

Michaud got it two years ago. Favert six months later. Yesterday, Tissayre. It's true that between Favert and Tissayre there was a large gap. M. de Stumpf-Quichelier having failed, despite the concerted efforts of his friends and two undersecretaries of state, to get himself promoted to commander, the normal march of promotions came to a halt. Not only all the Legion officers in our company were condemned to wait until the rosette blossomed in the chief's buttonhole, but various pretexts were made for avoiding any banquets of honor. This halt had to last for over a year, until the arrival of Fitz-Arnold. Finally, the chief procured his silver insignia and festivities were resumed.

Will I soon be the only man in my section not to have it? Such a thought doesn't unduly disturb me, but there

are moments when, amidst so many beribboned lapels, I
have the feeling of not being fully dressed. I'd like to be
able to pass it all off as a joke, to make light of it, like
Tailloret, who, at the end of this banquet, startled the
checkroom attendant by saying, "Give me the coat that
doesn't have the Legion of Honor"—but I'm not so good
at it as he. Probably it's Thérèse's fault, since she keeps
saying, "*You'll* never get it" or "Can't *you* get it, too?," as
if I were impotent. I already feel that on the day when I
get it she'll say to me, "Oh! Well, you've taken long
enough about it!"

My name must figure somewhere, on some list, of course.
But they must have forgotten me. This eternal phenomenon of transparency. From lists of honor students to those
of people entitled to special coupons during the occupation, I've known so many lists on which my name should
have featured but from which it was absent! If, on the
other hand, it's something like a census of unemployed
for compulsory labor or of those fit to bear arms, my name
is never missing.

For my part, I would never mention the Legion of
Honor to Thérèse if it weren't for those accursed banquets.
I have to explain why I'm dining out. I have calculated
that the Tissayre banquet was the twenty-third occasion
in ten years when I've told my wife, "I have a Legion of
Honor banquet tonight."

I guarantee on my word of honor that, out of these
twenty-three, only six were invented.

Like some other men of my kind, I like to declare, "As

for me, you know, decorations don't mean a thing. There's only one of any real value, the Military Medal" (I don't have that either), "or the Legion of Honor, of course—but then only for military service. Apart from that . . ."

Nevertheless, sometimes, musing about my death, I have a melancholy feeling when I reflect that in the obituary announcement no one will read that little phrase which has the ring of a sort of supreme good mark and enables those you leave behind to bury you with heads held high:

"He was a chevalier of the Legion of Honor."

8

POLITICS

O F COURSE I do!

I have always cherished a deep affection for international affairs—without receiving any reward for it, except for being mobilized once or twice. In spite of which, I continue to give it my devoted attention. What I may have to say about politics would in any event hardly amount to anything very striking. And these lines will never carry the weight of those statesmen's memoirs whose publication has multiplied so rapidly of recent years. Not everybody can write: "Sent today for von Mackensen to inform him we are in a state of war. Elisa brought me my beef tea. Tomorrow will be a crucial day for Europe and the whole world." No, I could never compare my jottings with the message of these supermen. I don't get up each morning with the idea of refashioning the world. My life, all in all, is made up of little things. But if you take a closer look at it, is there really such a difference between the little things and the big ones? Sometimes, while I'm scribbling

New scale of premiums
Miriam
Christmas shopping

in my desk diary, I reflect that at the same moment some Great Man ruling over 250 million souls is entering

New rocket
Germany
Israel

in his. Of course, you can't ask the leader of the Soviet world to jot down "Settle Saint-Gobain lawsuit" on his memorandum pad. The more important the job, the more one has to justify one's salary. And when one can't do anything with clients like Péchiney or Rhône-Poulenc, one does with what one has—Iran or the North Pole. Moreover, I imagine it must be intoxicating to be able to say, "I want you to launch a rocket to the moon on the twenty-fifth" (and be obeyed). But mankind will never have peace so long as any one gentleman is able to wake up somewhere in the world and say to himself, "Where shall I stir up a

132

little excitement today, Formosa or the Aleutians?" There precisely is someone not to be relied upon.

And so I sometimes find myself dreaming of a world in which the public services will be run by the U.S.A., interplanetary travel by the U.S.S.R., hygiene by Switzerland, cooking by France, and the police by England. Someday this world will exist. Unfortunately not in my day. Meanwhile, I take an interest in the situation by reading the papers like everyone else. (Most people ask, "You mean you really believe what they say in the papers?" but go on and buy them the next day nevertheless.) After many years' experience, I think I'm in a position to offer a few observations, the fruit of my reading:

1. *Reliable sources and generally well-informed circles.*

Every day a large number of dispatches are published which all begin as follows: "It is learned from reliable sources that . . ." or "According to generally well-informed circles, it is thought that . . ." The style of telegrams has doubtless changed since the days when they used to write: "His Majesty's Government is inclined to the view that the gravest misgivings should be entertained over . . ." (over the situation, of course), but Reliable Sources have not yet dried up and Official Circles are at a premium. From the care with which Reliable Sources are considered, I deduce that there exist certain fantastic or even comic ones which it is prudent to shun. (By the same token, when an American or Soviet strategist declares, "In the event of a serious conflict we shall not hesitate to use atomic weapons," one sees how one may easily lose one's life in numerous conflicts which cannot be regarded as serious.)

I've often wondered precisely what "official circles" are. Once, and only once, I'd like to read a dispatch in a paper running as follows: "It is learned from unreliable and generally ill-informed but nevertheless bona fide sources that His Majesty's Government, renouncing the sacrosanct weekend" (ritual cliché), "has met to conduct a superficial examination of the situation, for which, they have agreed, it is difficult to find an explanation." I don't count too much on this. In general, the experts prefer to explain. Suppose the leader of the Soviet Union vanishes tomorrow into the backwoods of Mongolia. A hundred experts will immediately explain how and why this came about. We would have liked to know it before, but we mustn't ask for too much. The same goes for gold. If it falls in value, they explain to us why. If it rises, they also explain why. In between, when we would very much like to know whether it's going to go up or down, they tell us nothing. We must just wait. For that, there is nothing like:

2. *Time (which works)*.

The Time Factor is of vital importance for the situation. For whom does time work precisely? Offering a (reliable) opinion on this subject is a delicate problem. Sometimes for the one, sometimes for the other; it's a rather merce-

nary factor. But in a general way rarely for France, v
it's reckoned that time always works for the other side

3. *The turning point.*

Clearly, if we are to believe what we're told, we're at a
Turning Point. Since when? Hard to say. For my part, I
would never have thought it possible to remain at a turning point for such a long time: exactly forty-five years. I
was born at a turning point. I was again told after getting
my baccalaureate that I was at a turning point. I turned
with the rest during the war, only to find myself back again
at a turning point after that upheaval, along with a number
of others, since when I hear it said every day that we're at
a turning point. (I'd be interested to know how many
editorials, since the world first began to turn, have been
headlined "The Last Turning Point" or "Not a Minute to
Lose.") It's not surprising, after all, that there are so many
accidents, since (as every driver knows) you can go five
miles in a straight line without seeing another car, only to
meet two head on at the first slightly tricky bend, both of
them driving on the wrong side of the road. Whatever my
natural disposition for living at a turning point, I'm getting quite used to the idea of dying at one.

4. *The fatal slope.*

Generally follows the last turning point—which is logical—but is preferably used to stress the perils of the economic situation.

135

Every three to five years since I made my first appearance here on earth, I've heard some V.I.P. declare that we're rolling down a fatal slope and that, but for the steps he's taking, we'd be heading straight for bankruptcy. If you consider that the French have been receiving the same warning from their finance ministers (not to mention all the others) since the days of Hugh Capet, you have to conclude that the slope, however fatal, is very skiable. For finally, since France has never to my knowledge gone into liquidation, one of two things must happen: either the tree trunk or bankruptcy recedes indefinitely or nobody ever tells us when we run into it.

I've gradually grown accustomed to driving tranquilly down this road to catastrophe, along which vigilant minister-policemen protect us from armed robbery by brigands, taking care to lighten our wallets themselves in advance. Lightening them by making them weigh even more with the new Heavy Franc, as they have recently done, constitutes, I must admit, a variation whose paradoxical nature I shall always appreciate. This achievement is choice, if not heavy, and well worth its weight in gold, even though it be only a few milligrams. (When you contemplate the declining scale of those little gold ingots whereby the statisticians pictorially represent our money, you wonder just how far they'll be able to go like this before it is too far.

Whatever, then, the force of the spectral images brandished to make us swallow each new pill—France in rags going through the world holding out her tin cup is one of the best of them—they don't tighten our hearts as easily as our belts. We know only too well that, after this new Last Turning Point, many more Ultimate and Final ones will be announced; the world will continue to turn, for all that—and France with it, more or less well clad. We still hear, over the months and years, the phrases which so many Premiers have made us hear. What gives such cause for wonder about their declarations is not only that they still find something to say but also that, to a nation in which skepticism has become a dominant feature, they can yet again speak of balancing income and expenditure without losing their composure. Their proposals are so perfectly reasonable, so even childishly logical, that you wonder why they never thought of them before. Were the legislators still unborn? Did France never progress before? You doubt it, for if so many elementary things remain to be done it must be because for at least a hundred years nobody has done very much about them.

"The government," declares each Premier, "has to set an example by achieving substantial economies." As if to say that hitherto the government was, with regard to economies, a little spendthrift. "A redistribution of office is necessary"; it would be difficult to make it plainer that our best men have up to now been scattered in places where they could do least good, and that the Minister of Posts, Telephone and Telegraph would make an excellent Undersecretary of State for Fine Arts. "We must apply drastic financial remedies"; did they use anemic remedies without our knowledge? Doubtless they did, because: "Our finances must be made sound and healthy, domestic and foreign

137

exchange invigorated, public confidence revived." You'd
swear that hitherto our governments frequented only third-
rate pharmacies and delighted in making the country live
in an unhealthy climate prescribed by quacks.

To return to our monetary reforms, they wouldn't annoy
me more than the next man if I didn't have to explain them
to Thérèse. It's sometimes tricky to explain to a woman
things you don't fully understand yourself, at the same
time conveying to her that while you understand them
perfectly, she isn't constituted to understand a great deal
about them. If only women would take things up from the
beginning, when we ourselves are learning them for our
own sakes, we would be prepared to explain them. But
they let a considerable time go by before resigning themselves to reading a few articles dealing with the return to
convertibility and the rights of transfer with regard to
property. Then come the headlines which force their attention (and ours); they ask us point-blank, in a tone
which brooks no hesitation, to explain to them in a few
well-chosen words what exactly is the freeing of exchanges
or the bread subsidy—and we're trapped.

As for the interest that the French in general, and those
in our apartment house in particular, take in political
affairs, again it's a question of understanding the way in
which this manifests itself. A poll taker from the Institute
of Public Opinion would no doubt be extremely hard put
in a time of acute crisis to draw up an accurate inventory
of the political affiliations in a company like mine. No one

would doubt that my colleagues were divided, but there are times when every Frenchman himself must be divided in two. With my own eyes I have seen M. Calisson, assistant technical director for "provincial casualties," come in one morning left of center and go off to dinner a Gaullist.

If, however, an expert sociologist applied himself to assessing the effects of an international crisis on the tenants in my building, he would be tempted to conclude that a state of high tension excites their gastric juices more than anything else, so true is it that, of all their organs, their stomachs react the most vigorously to threats of war or other grave complications. I myself have noticed that the first effect of a tense situation in the Middle East was to provoke my cotenants to rush for sugar, whereas, a few months later, the virulence of an upheaval in Africa gave rise to a stampede for new potatoes. No doubt it's difficult for the experts, always alert for the relations between cause and effect, to admit the interdependence of Port Said and beetroot, but the fact remains that as soon as the international situation becomes "grave" the apartments in our building transform themselves into so many grocery stores. From sugar to candles, via olive oil and macaroni, you can find in my neighbors' homes a little, or even a lot, of everything. Which they justify by saying, "What do you expect? Everything's so scarce!" Or take another development which would leave one flabbergasted did one not know that Butard's genius draws endless resources from penury: Accustomed to managing quite happily with two gallons of gas and quite used to running dry, he makes it a point of honor to have his tank full from the moment fuel is in short supply.

In the evenings during times of crisis my neighbors go out little. They prefer to have a few friends in to discuss the situation. Thus at the same moment in millions of different living rooms, experienced minds are brought by infallible logic to demonstrate that there will be war—"A little more orangeade?"—or that there will not be war. I sometimes have occasion to be a witness of these debates.

"I'm in a good position to know," declares M. Planchon, who makes biscuits at Nanterre but seems to have spent his day hiding behind an arras in the Kremlin, "that the Russian machine is beginning to crack up."

"Not at all," retorts M. Cussiez (fifth floor left). "They won't budge an inch."

"Anyway, a war over what?" asks M. Planchon. "Oil? As if we needed oil! Now, I'd drop Middle East oil altogether. Altogether! I'd get my oil from Hassi Messaoud and take it straight from England. On the way, I'd irrigate Spain. Yes, that's right, Spain! And what would be the result? A quarter of a million Spanish workers put on their feet! Nothing could be simpler."

What a pity such lucid minds aren't employed in higher posts! Wars prove to us that the world contains a small number of experts who are abreast of everything, know everything, can do everything—and say nothing, except in books that come out ten years later. But there are in the world about a million men who, every evening, give a million others the key—the only key—to the international situation, and the politicians are never among their number and never profit from their advice.

P.S.—Sent my last reply card tonight. Logically my aptitude for statistics should give me an advantage, since it's a question of figuring averages, but I'm not really nourishing much hope. Still, there are moments when the idea of victory flits furtively through my mind. The most skeptical contestant cherishes at some time the dream of winning the first prize, telling himself, "Why not me?" Thérèse, for her part, never ponders such matters. She continues to claim that I'm wasting my time, that I'd be better off doing . . . She finds all contests stupid, and this one in particular; the mere term *Average Frenchman*—like *middle class*—sets her teeth on edge.

When I consider the brevity of my replies, I realize that they have only a remote connection with these pages I have written.

I must confess that they don't all correspond to my private convictions. How, for instance, when asked what is the most outstanding quality of the French citizen, could one help extolling the one the whole world acknowledges, common sense? It goes hand in hand with good taste.

I don't know if there are other countries in the world with good taste, but I don't believe there is a single one so famous for its own which so often appeals to that of others. For proof, you need look no farther than the way in which so many apartments are furnished. My natural bent for

141

statistics, allied to the needs of a profession which, at the time when I wasn't yet an actuary, often obliged me to call on prospective clients, has led me to deduce that, out of a hundred French living rooms:

Eighty-two and four tenths include an impressive amount of Chinese, Japanese or Indochinese objects. When the Yellow Peril arrives it will feel completely at home. One would think every tenant had had a great-uncle who fought in the Far East and garnered a little table of black wood encrusted with mother-of-pearl or two pale-green vases enlivened by red tangerines. At least in those days people brought something back from the wars.

Seventy-two blend North Africa with China by the addition of one or two Moroccan pouffes of bright-yellow leather adorned with needlework.

In sixty-five the exotic element is completed, together with the inevitable red and rather worn Kurdish or Persian carpet, by a collection of Dresden china—harlequins, marquises, shepherdesses, all subjects of a tender conventionalism—scattered about on the embroidered and dusty Chinese shawl which covers the upright or grand piano (according to whether the apartments are on Staircase A or Staircase B). Sad enough in itself, this piano top on which a bust of Czerny (Poland) or Clementi (Italy) molders, awaiting the melancholy practicing of some disappointing and disappointed daughter, is in addition made even gloomier by yellowing photographs of half a dozen forebears, frozen for eternity in their wedding finery, uniforms or first-Communion veils.

142

I must, to be fair, acknowledge that in certain circles, better off financially and calling themselves more modern, China, North Africa, Dresden and Persia tend to be overshadowed by England. Indeed, in 32 per cent of the apartments visited I noticed a receptacle known as a "sea chest," when in fact the said chest is composed of two canteens, placed one above the other, which formerly belonged to infantry or cavalry officers, unless they came straight from a cabinetmaker on the Left Bank who specializes in "Regency." On the walls, fox-hunting scenes and colored prints depicting the adventures of Mr. Pickwick.

In ninety-two two by two Louis XV armchairs which, between China and Morocco, insure the perpetuity of our national furniture and testify to a secret affection for the monarchy. Some are signed, most are fake, about a dozen are signed and fake.

I have no doubt this assemblage, however heterogeneous it may appear at first sight, reflects the good taste of my fellow citizens. After all, these are only a few living rooms picked at random out of millions. I may well be wrong.*

---

* Even so, how can one deny the evidence? Leaving furniture aside, the French, distrustful by nature, have always loved what comes from distant lands, whether it be to clothe themselves or strip themselves: Eau de Cologne, Italian tailoring or Russian bonds. Didn't Balzac himself, referring to César Birotteau's Sultana's Pomade and Eau de Constantinople "which, like Eau de Cologne, was made in Paris," already say, "These place names were humbugs invented to please the French, who cannot tolerate things from their own country"? Nothing has changed since. When I want to buy my son a coat, the store catalogue gives me an embarrassing variety of choice between a suburban coat, an overcoat (with zip-in lining), a trench coat, a storm coat, a duffel coat, even a "school coat" more British than a member of the royal family, since it's reversible,

143

with herringbone tweed on one side and tartan on the other (models named Halifax, Richmond, Labrador, Blizzard, Johnny Popcorn and Big Top are, naturally, higher priced). To christen a car, our National Register doesn't hesitate to name it after an American state. And to make colors themselves more tantalizing, they are adorned with exotic labels: Singapore blue, Kilimanjaro white (so much whiter!), Trinidad red. Don't tell me, after all this, that the French are xenophobes, or, what with their Bahama yellow, Caspian gray and Borneo green, that they aren't strong on geography. Let's admit, rather, that if they put "Normandy green" or "Esterel red," it would have neither the same chic nor, no doubt, the same price. Should a Martian land in Paris (I hardly dare, in these modern or, rather, rocketing times, use the conditional to refer to so banal an eventuality), he would quickly realize how, from Sherpa tents to Tahiti bikinis, by way of Dovka coats and Teen-Form brassières, our proud but generous language multiplies the costs of imports.

9

THE
METAMORPHOSIS

I DID IT!

The incredible has come true.

I am "the Average Frenchman Number One."

And a millionaire twenty times over—provided I still count in old francs instead of new ones, which gives me an extra little kick.

Leaving aside the main questions which inspired me to jot down the foregoing reflections—of course reduced to their simplest form of expression in my replies—there were thirty-three of us (out of forty thousand) who found the correct answers to the secondary questions, which, as anyone knows, are of vital importance in a contest, like the luxuries in life. These concerned the average Frenchman's physical characteristics and his rate of consumption of various commodities. Out of the thirty-three survivors, ten corresponded point by point with the following description: height five feet nine and a half, blue eyes, chestnut hair, premature baldness, incipient adiposity, etc. I have to acknowledge that my capacities as a statistician certainly contributed largely to the fact that I stayed in the running with thirty-two rival candidates, although chance had never favored me to this extent before. But that I should form one of the ten finalists verged on the miraculous, pure luck—or the two combined. And finally, even if my calculations enabled me to hit it off with my 420 cups of coffee and my 35 annual cakes of soap, it is to luck at least as much as to my calculation of probabilities that I owe my having won by replying "2.3" to the question "How many children does the married Frenchman between the ages of twenty-nine and fifty have?" I was nearly sure of the 2. And even of a fraction more. But it was almost by pure guesswork that I added a point and a 3. A few days after I mailed my reply.(kept strictly secret) Thérèse confided to me that she was pregnant. I must confess, at the time the news brought me no pleasure. My first reaction was panic. I forgot the contest, my calculations, even my 2.3. I would have given anything to have this extra worry vanish out of my life.

During the night, however, the decimal point came back and I lay thinking about it. I woke up Thérèse and ˙asked her for detailed information. I wanted to know since when. Precisely. "Are you *sure?*" To owe success to a decimal point through the medium of a woman who has never had the faintest idea of punctuation seemed to me too illogical.

My anxiety gradually veered to hope. It remained to be seen whether the figure I had given corresponded to that of the general statistics of France for the period—and whether, among the ten contestants still in the running, others besides me had come close to it.

Today I know.

So does the whole country.

What a curious sensation, when you're used to obscurity as I am, to find yourself suddenly plunged into what is commonly called the glare of publicity!

It feels like being born a second time. It would hardly surprise me to read such an announcement as ".The birth is announced of M. Paul Blot, aged forty-five . . ." Seeing people seeing me as I am, I wonder if up to now they saw me as I wasn't. It's clear, for instance, that my features must have altered. They now notice that I have a nose, a mouth and even an expression. One writer who did a profile of me for *Paris-France* even went so far as to discern a glint of irony in my eyes, hitherto so lackluster. "M. Blot," he wrote, "exudes good health, honesty, stability. With his quietly confident gait, his slight tendency to stoutness and his bald patch, is he not the very image of the average Frenchman?" My "restrained gestures" are also emphasized. Strange. Strange, too, to see what was previously written off as banality, insignificance and grayness become a sense of proportion, modesty and, of course, common sense. Need I state that I am found to have common sense? Through me this praise is reflected on forty-three million Frenchmen; that always gives pleasure.

Common sense. Always common sense.

What is common sense, exactly? Larousse says: "The

ability to distinguish spontaneously between truth and
falsehood and to assess things at their true worth." But
when one Frenchman describes another as having common
sense, does he think of all that? I believe, rather, that if
he credits his neighbor with having good sense, it simply
means that he regards him as qualified to reason as he himself does—sensibly. Which flatters the qualifier as much
as the qualified. One could keep on telling the French they
have common sense every day for five hundred years and
they would still never tire of it (just as it tickles their vanity to hear it confirmed that they are a great nation). No
matter that they may change direction every six months
and worship a republic after a king, an emperor after a
republic, a monarchistic general after a socialist parliamen-
tarian, it's understood once and for all that they are the
nation of common sense—just as they are the people of
good living, good food and good form. There's nothing bad
in them except their livers.

That's why I never hesitated for a second, when answer-
ing the questionnaire, to put high above everything else—
together with good taste—the common sense of my fellow
citizens (not forgetting to stick on the envelope that post-
age stamp with the walleyed Marianne which I have always longed to see obliterated). After all, I should be in a
good position to know where I stand with regard to statistics. Everyone in my profession says that statistics are the
bikinis of the insurance companies—the important thing
is what they hide.

And common sense naturally came out on top.

148

From time to time I look at myself in a mirror and think: You are Blot, Paul Blot. You are exactly the same man as you were yesterday, and yet it took only one minute —one second really, the time it took you to write "2.3"— for everything to change. This face which only yesterday attracted nobody's attention, this figure which slipped through life like a shadow—here they are transformed into the cynosure of all eyes. People telephone me to ask my advice on the school vacation, capital punishment, fashions, the problem of Berlin. Me! Celebrity demands that one have an opinion on everything. Besides, the reporters aren't very exacting: "Tell me anything, Monsieur Blot. As long as I have something from you it's all right."

At meals I have noticed that Thérèse doesn't look at me as she used to before. It's as if she were saying, "It's too much. I thought I knew him, and then . . ." I couldn't guarantee that Thérèse's feelings aren't colored by a trace of resentment. She isn't exactly displeased that my name —and hers—should be headlined today in the press, but she has too often consigned me to the Devil to accept without a hint of mortification the sight of me shining like a film star being pestered for interviews. Happily for everybody, she has her share in the triumph: if she acknowledges in me the paternity of this victory, I can't deny her a certain claim to its motherhood.

Even the children no longer look at me with the same eye. There is not only pride and joy in their gaze but also a sort of worried astonishment, the kind of—who knows?— terror one feels before sacred monsters, or, more simply, the respect inspired in children by the word *million*. They too, no doubt, realize that they were mistaken—or that they have been misled about me. Their friends have opened their eyes. "Say, the man who won, is that your father?" And they said "Yes." And they felt strengthened by a paternal omniscience of which, only yesterday, they were unaware.

As for the changed atmosphere which the result of the contest has provoked throughout the whole of my firm, this is for me the equivalent of a revolution. Just as I no longer feel the same at home, I can't believe I've remained the same at the office. If, the day after the results were published, some of my superiors saw fit to affect indifference toward these extraprofessional pastimes, even a slight contempt for such a fuss about nothing, Hubert de Fitz-Arnold quickly changed their views by demonstrating in their presence to the chief the advantages to which the firm could turn this public promotion. Didn't our company's name appear in all the newspapers alongside mine? "You couldn't have done better if you had spent millions on publicity."

Since that moment the warmth of my welcome has been unanimous. And the little attentions are multiplying. S.Q. spoke to me not in a corridor, hurriedly, but in the middle of the Indian Ocean; for, apart from a brief moment when he veered over toward the Atlantic, the president-director general, receiving me in his office, remained standing before his gigantic luminous wall map, between the coasts of India and Arabia. He was going to confess something to me: For a long time now he had been considering my abilities and finding them insufficiently exploited. What astonished him was not the sight of them being crowned by public success but the fact that his closest colleagues hadn't thought of extending the sphere of my activities long ago. As for him ("Have I ever concealed it from you, my dear Blot?—I know I can count on you!"), he had always thought I was worth something better. The firm had the most pressing need of men with abilities like mine; I constituted one of its gilt-edge securities.

The very next day I was invited to "morning tea," the name given by Fitz-Arnold to the superselect get-together which is held every morning between ten-thirty and eleven in the chief's office. Such privileges, like the fact of having attended the king's levee, are known within minutes on every floor.

I now form one of what in high places are known, American style, as the yes men; that is to say, I have the right to approve what the president-director general says during a get-together or at a full-scale staff meeting, by articulating, "Yes—why, yes, certainly," whereas formerly I was just a nod man merely authorized to acknowledge without uttering. Barnage, who senses which way the wind is blowing, no longer has me summoned to his conferences by his secretaries; he calls me up himself with all kinds of precautions: "I know your time is precious just now, my dear friend" (I'm everybody's dear friend the whole day long), "but could you spare a moment to come to my office?" The "for me" has completely faded away; two weeks have now elapsed since anyone has said, "Get it done for me by tomorrow!"

Not only does Gaslin no longer annex my ideas, but these assume a weight which I myself would never dare give them. Thus my suggestion that the sending of the traditional New Year's greetings should be replaced by a card bearing the best wishes of the company to each of its policyholders on his birthday was the object of a unanimous vote of approval at a staff meeting.

Finally—supreme consecration—I was honored by a banquet. At the very heart of it this time, in the center of the table of honor, on the right of the president-director general, like Tissayre that night when they decorated him with the Legion of Honor. And like Tissayre, like all the others, I felt the sweet shower of platitudes descending on my head. If on this occasion the chief didn't have to look for the heart of gold beneath the rough exterior, he was no less agile in finding what I kept hidden beneath a shyness which might have led people to think me lacking in self-confidence: miracles of ingenuity, a passion for figures, the genius of precision. He ran the whole gamut: I was the Tireless Worker whose devotion to the common cause was rivaled only by my complete disregard for my health; the farsighted colleague; the most devoted member of our Big Family, the man of integrity, the true-friend-whose-dazzling-success-brought-glory-to-the-whole-firm. Not forgetting to associate my Dear Helpmeet with this success—always because of that decimal point.

Sitting in the speaker's shadow, beaming, bemused,

blissful, now and then tickled by some epithet sweeter than the rest, I wouldn't have been in the least surprised had I heard the chief conclude, "In the name of the President of the Republic and by virtue of the powers which are invested in me . . ."

No. That was not for tonight. But as the festivities were drawing to a close, Hubert de Fitz-Arnold took me into a corner and, taking hold of the buttonhole of my jacket, said, "Well, that little red ribbon—it won't be long now!"

That night, after I had returned home, I looked at myself again in the mirror. And I thought of the *Mona Lisa.* Not with any notion of resemblance, of course, but by a simple association of ideas. This *Mona Lisa* is admired the world over, yet how many people would consider her worthy of occupying the place of honor in the Louvre if they came upon her amidst a lot of bric-a-brac in a junkshop? A few connoisseurs, no doubt, but how many ordinary passers-by? And all those mutilated capitals, those truncated stumps of columns, those armless and legless statues—if the triple stars in the guidebooks and the voices of the guides didn't draw visitors' attention to them, who would look at them twice? The essential thing is to be consecrated.

Consecrated? I couldn't wish to be more so. Every day I am visited by reporters, photographers and interviewers, come to bank up the votive fires.

What is so annoying is that they never get me to talk

about what I know: life insurance, figures, statistics. What they want are anecdotes. Just like those princes whose photographs line the walls of my daughter's room and who used to seem so inaccessible, here am I, beset in turn by this mania for trivia.

"Haven't you any amusing story to tell?" asked one television reporter. "Something a little out of the ordinary?"

"!"

"Well, now. What is your principal childhood memory?"

I think. I rack my brains. I have the impression of opening a series of drawers as empty as those in a hotel room one has just vacated and around which one throws a last glance to make sure nothing has been left behind (though there may still be something there, left by the previous occupant). My life seems like an empty shell.

The reporter tries to help me. "What about your everyday life? Nothing that strikes you in particular? For example, do you count sheep when you can't sleep?"

Here's another thing that comes from America. There are more and more people who claim (in interviews) that they can get to sleep only by counting imaginary sheep jumping over a hedge. I've tried it: nothing leaves me wider awake; when a sheep escapes, I feel obliged to get up and go in search of it.

The reporter takes me back to school. "Did you already have a passion for figures then?"

"Er . . ."

"Were you well-behaved?"

"No."

"Were you very rowdy?"

"No."

"It's just what I was writing earlier: In order to hold the reporter's interest, like that of the teacher in the old days, I would have had to be either one or the other. My visitor seems desperately upset that I was an average, colorless pupil. He tries to get at me obliquely:

"Have you any hobbies?"

I tell him—rather shyly, for fear of creating a bad impression—about the horses, racing, the gentle pleasure I get from studying form and working out the odds. I think this penchant for gambling, which doubtless doesn't accord with his general notion of an actuary, may be what he's looking for. Yes . . . No, that's not at all what he wanted; you see, it's difficult to get a horse into the TV studio.

"Don't you collect anything? One of the last people I interviewed, he collected crusts of bread. He had a crust from the occupation, one from the liberation, a victory crust, a crust from 1870 and even a Roman crust dug up at Alesia. Now, that was really amusing!"

Far be it from me to disagree, but I'm forced to confess that I have no such crust for the reporter to dig his teeth into.

He's well aware of this. "Oh, I'm not suggesting, of course, that you should produce the same thing, but, well, I don't know—what about butterflies, matchboxes, cigar bands?"

Decidedly, I must be utterly devoid of originality; the idea that I might appear on the television screen without providing anything apart from myself seems to leave the reporter transfixed. He would like to give me time to think about it—I'll surely find something eventually.

No sooner has he gone than his place is taken by a photographer from a weekly, accompanied by two young men bearing wires, bags and flash bulbs.

"I won't be long," says the overlord photographer. "What I need, you understand, is a picture a little out of the ordinary."

"Not at my desk?"

"Oh, that would be too dreary! No, something like— well, you're alone, you've had enough of checking figures, enough of statistics, you want to stretch yourself. So you take off your tie and *relax!* You lie down on the floor—we want to get something natural. Have you a robe? Something in velvet, for instance?"

Dismissing as a matter of course the one place where I feel at ease in my office, that is to say my desk, and making me sit on the floor with my legs crossed in a position of acute discomfort, the photographer adds, "Above all, look relaxed. Robert, hand me the lamp. Just let yourself go and smile, Monsieur Blot.* Smile!"

---

* *The radio makes people more familiar. In the beginning they called me "Monsieur Blot." This very quickly became their "dear Monsieur Blot." The day before yesterday, the interviewer started off by suppressing the "Monsieur" altogether: "Here we are once again in the home of the celebrated Paul Blot." Then, in the heat of his interview: "Over here, my dear Blot—you don't mind, do you?" What could I say? That I did mind? So I smiled, which he must have taken to indicate tacit assent, for from then on he persistently called me "my dear Paul," "Paul, old man," and plain "Blot."*

How I envy those young men, or those politicians, who always find a way to smile even in rain, in snow or after the failure of a conference.

"Oh, come on, now, smile! There must be odd moments when you *do*."

It's true. Only just now I was laughing, I forget what at, doubtless nothing. But my smile has fled, I can't recapture it any more than the name of the man I know perfectly well but whom I suddenly have to introduce to someone else at the theater. I think of the smiles of Maurice Chevalier, Khrushchev, the Presidents of the Republic . . .

"Smile, just for the hell of it!" implores the photographer—but the moment I'm commanded to smile my face becomes paralyzed and my forced grimace merely reflects a hideous contraction of the zygomatic muscles. He gets impatient, tries to make me laugh, appeals to my good fortune, my success: "Come, now. We're pleased, we're happy, fortune smiles on us. We are the King of the Average Frenchmen, we have won twenty millions—in ten years' time it will be thirty! Ha ha!"

I must look dismal, for:

"You remind me of poor L . . . Impossible to make him laugh! 'Smile, monsieur, smile,' I used to tell him. Hopeless—he looked even more wretched. 'I never smile,' he said to me. A week later he was assassinated, poor man. Now, then, smile, if you please!"

Is it the paradoxical effect of this macabre story? I smile. A rather disillusioned smile, but it suffices. Click-clack.

That's it. No. The flash bulb hasn't flashed. We start again. My smile is now even more forced. Click-clack. The shutter has stuck. And I moved.

"If only I had my Paraflex! That never goes wrong."

With professional photographers, something always goes wrong. Now, when I take a photo I make a mess of it, granted. But I don't begin all over again. And so nobody is inconvenienced.

At last it's over. At least, so far as the smile in private relaxation goes. But I sense that something is still lacking. Something more original.

The photographer broods. "Now," he finally says, "would it be too much to ask you to jump?"

"*Jump?*"

"Yes. You must have heard about jumpomania? Just a little jump up and down like Mauriac, like Audrey Hepburn. It's most important for the psychiatrists."

Can he be serious? Oh, well, since Mauriac has done it . . . I gather myself together and jump idiotically up and down. If this can be of any use to the psychiatrists' statistics . . .

Even now we're not finished. The photographer evidently is hesitating as to whether or not he should ask me a question. At least, he seems to be groping for words.

"Forgive me, Monsieur Blot, but . . . haven't you . . . I don't mean to say a mannerism . . . but some personal trick, some particular attitude or gesture? For instance . . ." Then, suddenly pointing his finger at me: "Hold that position you're in now!" he cries as if he has just discovered America.

Sitting debating what I could offer the man by way of a trick or mannerism, I had automatically raised my right hand behind the nape of my neck and was questioningly fingering the bald patch at the back of my head.

"Perfect!" said the photographer. "That's exactly what I wanted. Monsieur Blot, excuse me, but do you do that often?"

Only too often, no doubt, I explained, since this passion for rubbing the back of my head unfailingly irritates Thérèse.

"Marvelous!" said my visitor, and he flashed.

This light massage of the skull followed by a gentle incursion of thumb and forefinger into the northern regions of the forehead is, according to one of these young men, a gesture common to many Frenchmen afflicted with baldness. "Thanks to you, Monsieur Blot, millions of people who unconsciously do exactly the same will find themselves reflected in our picture of you."

These young men, by dint of their efforts, had made me trusting. I was well on the way to making confession. I confided to them that often, descending from these occipital heights, my right hand passed gently down the side of my face; I was given to rubbing my eyelids, sometimes till my eyes ran, and, pressing both cheeks between fingers and thumb, squeezing down along my jawbone to the tip of my chin, winding up with a gentle pressure on each side of my nose which allowed me to enjoy inhaling the scent of the tobacco staining my fingertips. This gave me a fleeting, secret sense of well-being; I felt cleaner and better prepared to face life.

159

They cut my headlong account short: they had quite enough as it was.

This gentle massaging of my skull will doubtless be forgiven by Thérèse as soon as it has been sanctioned by a photograph published in two million copies. All my little tricks, formerly so staunchly opposed, are now tolerated when they're not positively praised.

Everything, right down to my reading of *Sport-Complet* and *Paris-Turf*—hitherto confined (concealed inside a respectable newspaper) to the secrecy of the bathroom—is now permitted in broad daylight. Only yesterday treated as a good-for-nothing who went off and secretly gambled away the housekeeping money, I have today become— again it's a journalist who put it best—"the judicious calculator who does not scorn, once his daily task is done, to weigh up the chances of his beloved quadrupeds and, through skillful permutation, increase his modest patrimony without ever placing the balance of the family budget in peril."

As for the occupants of my building, they fall into three categories: the sympathetic, the indifferent and the jealous. I shall say little of the first category, such as the concierge, who has never been involved in such a fiesta before and whose name has already appeared four times in the press. But I can hardly feel surprised at the bad temper displayed by M. Boiseron, who occupies the second-floor right. He entered the contest and failed even to place, and now the television people come and ask him if they may run through his window the cables which transmit my image to millions of viewers. Obviously, none of this ceaseless coming and going of cameramen, photographers and reporters, together with the trucks parked outside our main entrance, the flocks of inquisitive bystanders this engenders and the daily sight of my name in the papers, is designed to provoke a friendly fellow-feeling—either from him or from a great many others who also find it hard to swallow the fact that they were wrong about me and that fame has elected to crown the most insignificant occupant of the building. Stirred to indignation by this unseemly publicity, Mme. de la Lussardière has sent the landlord a blistering letter: "Why, just because a certain Blot" (as if to say "unborn") "has won some contest or other, do the private lives of the occupants of this building have to be thrown into a state of turmoil?" She even went so far as to allude to disturbing sounds of love making (one senses an appetite for legal proceedings over party walls and breach of the close). The letter was countersigned by several other tenants, including those on Staircase C, which gives ample proof of their bad faith, since the television people and the newspapermen never come up that way.

10

MINDING

OUR MANNERS

HERE I AM, in spite of myself, caught up in a whirlwind of galas, cocktail parties and receptions. Yesterday nobody even knew our name; today every mail brings its contingent of letters and invitations, which Thérèse sticks—she knows this is the correct thing to do—around the frame of the mirror over the mantlepiece. "Just to remind you . . . Comtesse de Lussy-Blangeac . . . dinner on the twenty-eighth . . . black tie." "Philippe and Sophie Langlade . . . the twenty-ninth, 6 to 9 P.M., for cocktails." All these new intimate friends want to be able to say they have had the Blots—"You know, the Average Frenchman Number One." We've become the main attraction of the moment.

I'd like to say no and refuse all these invitations. But Thérèse urges me to accept. If you don't go anywhere, she says, you don't get anywhere. And she reels off the names of a mass of people who have "arrived" in life only through having connections. Connections are everything—at least, everything at present. There's always something which Thérèse assures me is "everything." "Money is everything," she used to tell me when we didn't have any. "Work is everything," she told me at times when I didn't appear to be animated by exceptional energy. Sometimes luck was everything, sometimes it was self-confidence, sometimes common sense, when it wasn't children or the home. I realized long ago that everything was everything (and vice versa). The content simply varies with the mood, circumstances and whatever I don't possess in sufficient quantity to please Thérèse. At the moment, then, connections are everything. No opportunity must be missed.

For myself, I would sacrifice a great deal to avoid the galas and the nocturnal festivities, all those Nights with a capital N whose prime effect is to leave one a minimum of sleep—at least in my eyes, which have a tendency to close just as these Nights are beginning. This is, of course, the reaction of a stupid homebody who thinks that the night was devised for sleeping. What can I do about it? When I have steered my way through one of these Big Nights, nothing gives me such pleasure as to have a little night all to myself. Thérèse, who is indefatigable, maintains that she is forced to drag me everywhere, calls me a stay-at-home and declares that it's a waste of time living in Paris if you aren't in the swim. We might as well, she says, move to Angoulême or Bar-le-Duc.

I wonder if she isn't becoming just a little snobbish.

I can readily see how owning a car gives her a blissful feeling of independence. (She now regards as indispensable so many purchases which would previously have seemed to us the height of luxury, that I've begun to wonder what would have happened without this shower of millions.) I can also easily appreciate that the use of a check book confers on her the authority of which she always used to dream, and how she feels more at ease with a parlormaid who addresses her in the third person than she did with our former cleaning woman. But how could I have foreseen that Thérèse would one day be haunted by a desire to be included in what the press calls "Tout-Paris" (no doubt because it refers only to a tiny section of the capital)? Yet so it is. She never reads "Here in this ballroom the cream of Paris' loveliest women were to be seen" without contraction of the heart—that is, if she wasn't there herself. She has even begun to talk to me of social standing. Apparently I have to maintain a certain standing. She dreams of an apartment in one of the most fashionable districts (as per the realty agents' advertisements, which never refer to low standing), without Staircases A, B and C, and urges me to move. I suspect her of a certain fastidiousness over telephone exchanges. ROQuette gives her a complex. She would prefer AUTeuil or INValides.

I try to gain time by pointing out to her that it would hardly be seemly for people in our position to flaunt a change in our fortunes so blatantly. Socially, the problem is not easy. If I do nothing at all to alter my way of living, I'll be branded a miser. And if I order an American car, I'll be accused of letting the whole thing go to my head. We have to try to maintain ourselves at a happy mean. But here I'm touching on a sensitive spot. The fact that my success is based on our very averageness, and that this is brought up everywhere each day, does tend to cast a faint shadow over Thérèse's joy. This averageness riles her. Even so, she might remind herself that it's already a great deal to be exceptional in one's averageness; but doubtless she would have preferred the more solid fame of a Nobel Prize.

Can it be that this notoriety has turned her head more than mine? Even her vocabulary has changed. She falls a prey to new ailments which I for one had never heard of before—at least not under such names as nervous breakdowns, allergies and so on. Dangerous. The more so since neither of us is equipped to belong to this society, from which we used to feel excluded and to which I feel no more drawn today than I did before.

I'm becoming gradually more aware of this every day. I thought my vacation might procure me a certain respite. Not at all. On this southern beach invitations rain down on us. The whirlwind continues. There's only one difference: the salons are floating ones.

We were invited to spend twenty-four hours on the yacht of Mr. Demetriades Paparakis, a wealthy Greek shipowner who devotes his summer to entertaining all the best-known people on the coast. Would to God I had never gone aboard that galley! It cost me the bitterest of humiliations.

Friends had told us, "Above all, be sure to wear shorts. Raki loathes any kind of formality." So we went in shorts, taking with us only a little overnight case with our toilet necessities and the lightest of accessories.

In this garb, then, Thérèse and I went for a stroll on deck in the morning. We were early. No one else was up yet, except for a young man whom I had noticed the night before, during cocktails, because of his facetious high spirits. He now came up to us and started a conversation.

"I believe we're all going to lunch with Lady Carrington on her island—that one over there."

"Oh?" I said. "I thought we were putting out to sea.* Perhaps I ought to go back to the hotel and change."

"It's not for me to say," said the young man with a glint of irony, "but I think you should. Lady Carrington is rather a stickler over dress. Besides, one may always meet people. I'm fairly sure the Gaudrets will be there—do you know the Gaudrets?"

"Gaudret? Gaudret?" I said, pretending to think.

Whereupon Thérèse, driven by some hideous social vanity or else tormented by one of her new complexes, cried, "Of course! Paul, you know perfectly well. Gaudret —you're always telling me about him when you come back from the Auto." This is one of her manias; she wants me to become a member of the Automobile Club, she finds it gives "standing," and meanwhile she talks as if I already belonged to it. "Certainly, monsieur, he's one of my husband's oldest friends!"

A little silence. Then the young man laughed more mockingly than ever.

"How very odd," he drawled. "He's my caretaker."

Thérèse laughed, and so did I, but it was a very forced,

---

*I have since learned that on yachts of this type you go practically everywhere except out to sea.

167

Bernard Buffet

rather shrill laugh, one of those laughs that make your jaws ache.

Never in my life had I felt so ridiculous. I could see that this story, repeated at our expense, would go the rounds of the whole beach in a few hours. "Have you heard the latest about the Blots? James told them that Monsieur Gaudret was going to be lunching at Lady Carrington's. That's his caretaker, ha, ha, ha!"

Thérèse invented a sick headache and we returned to land without looking back. This was a lesson. If only it would cure her! But when you begin to get society life under your skin, ridicule can no longer kill.

The torture of invitations goes on and on. In spite of my training, I feel less and less at ease. To begin with, there are the introductions. "Monsieur Cercamp-Paveline, Monsieur Blot . . . Monsieur Blot, come with me, I want to introduce you to Orlane de Saint-Graban. Monsieur Blot, Madame de Saint-Graban." Faced with these double-barreled patronymics, which sound like the names of famous wines and bear the stamp of vast family estates and turreted castles, my monosyllabic name has an odd sort of ring. A modest little *vin rosé* strayed into the world of Veuve Clicquot and Mouton Rothschild, it seems to fall with a dull plop into an ocean of nobility.

"I want to introduce you to the van Cliffs. They're dying to meet you."

And I am dragged to the other end of the room. I am introduced; I set off again. Not without sometimes overhearing "But he's divine!" in a tone of voice which also implies "What an odd-looking man!" or simply "What a bore!" I feel that from tomorrow on the name of Blot will be on a hundred different tongues. "Guess whom I met yesterday at the Brimonts. The Blots! You know, the man who has been chosen Average Frenchman Number One. Incredible! What? Well, you know the sort of people one meets here."

If it were only the introductions! But there is also the noise, that parrot-house screeching. I don't know what marks our century will leave on history, but it's making enough noise while it's going on—even more than any other century. If it were true that noise can kill I would have been in my grave long ago. But it doesn't kill everybody. On the contrary, one would swear that it helps society to live. For proof I need only cite the behavior of these people, who hate the uproar of the Métro but rush to find the very same uproar in select spots where it's called atmosphere. (I love going to night clubs; it cures me of any desire to go back for a whole year.) And before my eyes, not to say my ears, I have the example of my daughter, who seems unable to take in Tacitus or Sallust unless a calypso by Belafonte or a rock 'n' roll by Elvis Presley is bawling in the background.*

Among all the deafening inventions which are slowly

---

* Which produces the following, almost word for word: "Majores nostri . . . darling, I love you . . . patres conscripti . . . you sweetheart . . . neque consilii . . . boum badabam geegee! . . . neque audaciae . . . oh, baby!" A Seneca rocked and rolled did not form any part of my childhood curriculum; it must be her age, if not her sex.

killing me with decibel blows, the cocktail party is one of the most lethal. Here again, other people aren't made the way I am, since they never seem to talk so much as when they can't hear each other.

Finally, I'm so ill-adapted to the standing position. I'll never learn how to clutch a glass in one hand and a snack in the other and at the same time be relaxed, smiling, eloquent, adept at shifting the weight of my body from one leg to the other, and able to hold several people breathless with my ideas of Picasso, *musique désincarnée*, flying saucers or leukemia. A disjointed puppet, I just concentrate on keeping my balance, trying to make out what my neighbor is yelling at me amidst the surrounding tumult. True, I'm equally ill-adapted to the seated position at dinner parties, with its obligation to swing from right to left at regular intervals. The movement from right to left and vice versa and the soup-to-cheese gradation of a conversation skillfully divided between two ladies constitute for me an exhausting piece of social acrobatics. Besides, I have to find something to talk about. What is most painful of all is the opening gambit, the lead-in. Most often, what I try to say, such as "Have you been out much lately?," "Have you seen the Ballets du Marquis?," "We're not having much luck with the weather," strikes me as so empty and futile that I prefer to throw in the sponge. This is a grave mistake. The longer I wait before speaking, the less desire I have to do so. I soon regret not having taken the plunge earlier. My own silence paralyzes me. It's a creeping numbness. My ladies have already been caught up in conversation with their next-door neighbors on the other side—and I'm left alone with my plate.

Sometimes I dive in; three stupid words, barely sufficient to break the ice, emerge from my gullet. Oblivious of the laws of social equilibrium, my one concern is to maintain contact with the lady to whom I have managed to say something, while pursued by remorse for not talking to the other. I was already bored myself, but my boredom, increased by that of this lady, becomes intolerable. True, the lady on my other side, whom I've abandoned, doesn't always sit there unmoved. One night I was called to order by a lady whom I had never met before but who was none the less brusque for all that. As I was devoting too much attention for her liking to her counterpart on my right, she suddenly said, "Tell me, dear Monsieur Blot, did you ever learn how to drive on the left?"

What wouldn't I give to avoid such scenes! But Thérèse is insatiable.

"If it were left to you," she says, "we'd never go anywhere and no one would ever visit us."

It's possible. That would suit me fine. I like dinner parties as little in my own home as in other houses. But, as Thérèse says, we have to reciprocate. And so we keep giving boring dinners for people in whose houses we were bored a month before.

11

THE KINGDOM
OF THE SNOBS

I'D LIKE to fall in with Thérèse's wishes. But even with the best will in the world I'm sure I'll never really be able to form part of this high society. The feeling I get of being alien to it springs first and foremost from the fact that I don't speak the same language. I had fresh proof of this only the other evening:

As the conversation after dinner revolved around the subject of weekends, a gentleman suddenly turned to me and asked, "And you, Monsieur Blot, what's *your* game?"

I gaped at him. What with the mania society people have for talking in a sort of telegraphese of their own, I couldn't make out whether he was referring to recreation, hunting or eating—or whether he was questioning my purpose in being there.

My expression must have conveyed something to my questioner, for, without giving me time to reply, he concluded, "Ah, so you don't play golf."

Being thus written off, I got the feeling I didn't amount to much in the eyes of this man, who was obviously

Alors, vous êtes golf!

puzzled as to how the devil I managed to kill my Sundays.

No, decidedly, all things duly considered, I'm in no way equipped to conquer the kingdom of the snobs. I have neither the right language, the bearing, the gestures, the detachment nor the face.

Certain essential faculties are lacking in me. My mania for classification, added to an already appreciable experience, here permits me to draw up a list of them:

1. A *blasé air*.

What perhaps strikes me most about the Right People is their air of boredom. Is it the fact of being able, it would seem, to have everything they want in life which makes them so morose? Or is this blasé air simply good form? I can't be sure but very often they appear to be frustrated. The more the place where they are is renowned for its atmosphere, the more bowed down they look. And when they don't meet many others made in their own image, as sad as a gray winter's day, they complain that there's no atmosphere. Nothing is so disconcerting as to see people amusing themselves with the semblance of complete boredom. Clearly, whatever the efforts I made to look sad while enjoying myself, I'll never manage to reflect this state of permanent dejection.

In restaurants, at least in those de luxe restaurants where it's important to be seen, they never for a moment drop this dismal air. You get the feeling that they're appallingly tired of having to order melon ("But only if it's absolutely ripe!") or poached trout (". . . and above all be sure nobody touches it, won't you?").

M. de Fitz-Arnold, with whom I was lunching yesterday in a smart restaurant, had this same look. With a jaundiced eye he gazed at Charlie Chaplin, the Prince of Asturia and Audrey Hepburn, whom he seemed to find very commonplace. One would have sworn he saw them every day. ("If you want to be left in peace," a film star pestered by requests for autographs once said to me, "you have to go to the most expensive restaurants—there they all pretend not to recognize you.") The waiter was waiting. M. de Fitz-Arnold wasn't ready. The waiter withdrew. Fitz-Arnold complained, "There's never anyone to take your order here. Sommelier!" He belongs to that species of customer who never really feels properly treated unless three waiters stay leaning over him like weeping willows, making enticing suggestions which he doesn't follow. In addition, he won't feel completely at ease until the moment when someone runs up to announce, "Rome on the telephone for you, monsieur." Delighted, but to all outward appearances most annoyed that Rome should disturb him, he gets up, taking his time, thereby proving that to him money means nothing and Rome, like everything else, is a bore.

Just as we were leaving, a friend of Fitz-Arnold waved to him and, in a disillusioned voice which floated across several heads called, "I'm off to New York this afternoon," as if he were going there for tea. "Any message you'd like me

to take?"* Then I heard the commissionaire behind me mutter waggishly to a waiter, "Off to Montmartre this afternoon. Any words for the birds?"

2. *The manner of dress.*

I noticed it once again this summer: whatever these people choose to wear, it has chic. When black swimming trunks were the fashion, black swimming trunks fitted them like a glove. This year it's multicolored shorts printed with skyscrapers, palm trees and fish; it still becomes them. I've tried buying a pair myself, but if others can walk around exposing the Empire State Building on the left buttock and a sea horse on the right ("I got it for an absolute song at Acapulco!") without anyone considering it ridiculous, I have the feeling, in this same garb, of being the main attraction of the beach. Moreover, even if I confine myself to sober hues, I always look as if I were in disguise. I don't become myself again until I put on my jacket. They seem to have been born in their shorts. Come the evening, here they are again, equally at ease in their white dinner jackets. They never look as if they were decked out in fancy dress; their clothes are a second skin.

The sun permeates their skin in the same way: it filters through. However much I change my sun cream or oil, I never manage to get a tan like these privileged beings, who

---

* It is equally good form in this type of American-style restaurant (Hamburger on Toast, Oyster Stew) to scribble little notes which one gets the waiter to transmit to friends ("Just take this over to Monsieur Jimmy Barclay . . .").

are cooked through and through to a gentle brown, in winter by the sun of Arlberg, in summer by that of the Balearics: their skin has such a metallic sheen, you would think they had had it dipped in gold.*

Here's another of these phenomena of osmosis to which I remain allergic: My pallid calves, thinly strewn with black hairs, seem to refract the rays of the sun, and through the front of my open sandals project stubbornly white toes.

That—to say nothing of the effect made by the budding *embonpoint* of my stomach in my beige shorts—is why Thérèse suffers for me in summer on the beach. Here I appear out of place more than ever. This is not only my judgment, but also that of the Right People; last year, on another beach some smart people murmured, "Wonder where *he* came from," as they watched me go by.

3. *The way of expressing oneself, using certain English words.*

How could I ever hope to possess the verbal ease of this intelligentsia which speaks a fluent French heightened at just the right moment by a subtle use of English? It isn't only a question of the phrases in which English is indispensable and in which, therefore, you have to use the correct accent—for example, the way (doubtless acquired from birth) to ask for *"un whisky* on the rocks," to say that

---

* *I was struck one day by the following sentence in an American detective novel: "He had speculated so much in steel that his eyes had developed a metallic glitter." At first sight I found this absurd. Now I'm not so sure.*

you've had yourself "*checké*" by your "medico," to inquire
of a hostess, "Black tie *ou veston?*" or to describe a woman
as "*très* sexy." This accent also persists in the Frenchest of
French—at least in what it's good form to leave in French,
once you've allowed for English, Italian and slang: "*Je vais
prendre un* snack *en vitesse avec Bill et nous allons faire un
peu de* surfing—O.K.? *Ciao!*" In the same way, if Bill confi-
dently murmurs, "*Dites donc vous savez quoi? James a un
serieux* ticket *avec la petite Martínez*"—a formula which
has replaced the outmoded "He's been badly bitten by
. . ." and which adds a whiff of automation to the Anglo-
Saxon chic—you can see how this couldn't possibly be revealed without a pronounced British accent.

Whenever I myself try to use them, the same thing
happens with all these English words as with the clothes I
was talking about just now. Whether it's due to my
timidity or to my lack of training, they hang no better on
my lips than do the shorts on my hips. All I have to do is
decide to use one of them for it to be the wrong one. One
day I ventured a "Bye-bye." My son told me that nobody
uses that any more—even the English say "*Ciao.*"

Everything about the vocabulary of these Right People
baffles me. Will Thérèse, by dint of mixing with them, end
up by calling me "my lad"? It's possible, for "my lad"
seems very much the thing just now. I've heard more than
one distinguished lady say of her husband, "My lad's tuck-
ing into a steak" or "My lad lost an absolute packet at
solo"—this card game, which I thought purely proletarian,
having become very "fash'nable." These people are con-

summate artists at adopting from time to time words and
games hitherto reserved for the common people. Again,
you have to be well up on all this and know which ones.

4. *A perfect knowledge of the world of high society and*
   celebrities.

If the accent to which I've been referring eludes me, this
is because I'm not helped by that familiar knowledge of
the Anglo-Saxon world possessed to the nth degree by this
elite which is as accustomed to going to New York as I am
to Fontainebleau. Only this knowledge can permit you to
ask in the most natural way possible, if it's a question of
skiing, "Do you do the Rocheuses?"

I'd give a great deal to know the world the way these
champions of society do. Take, for instance, America or
England. There are some innocents who waste all their
time exploring the Far West, North Dakota or the Orkney
Islands, and after they have covered tens of thousands of
miles they confess that there still remains a great deal for
them to see. This is absolutely not the case of those superior beings of whom I'm speaking. Familiarity with a mere
few hundred square yards, let's say the extent of five or six
Paris *arrondissements,* is enough for them to know all
that's necessary of the world, at least of the world that
counts. Does their conversation turn to New York or London? Naturally they don't start enthusing over the pigeons
in Trafalgar Square or the skyscrapers on Wall Street like
any country bumpkin, but (how much more soberly)

186

they'll say that they met Mike at Twenty-one, bought a nice selection of ties and silk handkerchiefs in Jermyn Street, or attended the opening of a new gallery on Fifty-seventh near Fifth. Knowledge of a rectangle of Manhattan the size of the Place Vendôme enables them to say much more about America than someone who has visited the Wahoupi Indians. Nothing escapes their vigilance. The scale of social values holds no secrets for them; it's based on infallible landmarks which remain mysteries to me. Witness the following conversation I recently overheard:

"They're staying at the Waldorf-Astoria. You know the type?"

"Ah, yes."

"No, not at the Waldorf-*Astoria*," someone else corrected. "The Waldorf *Tower*."

"Oh, that's better!"

In this way I learned that to stay at the Waldorf Tower (one of the cubes which surmount the main building) is not at all the same thing as just staying at the Waldorf. One simply has to know. The cosmos of Right People seems to me as vast as it is limited.

On the beaches where they converge from Paris, Mexico, London and Caracas, everyone seems to have known everyone else from tender childhood, and yet I know that many of them never met till the night before.

Barely has a yacht revealed its sail on the horizon when one hears:

"That's Juan" (pronounced Rrhouan'n) "coming back

187

from Cannes with the Higginses. I say, his jib seems to have been knocked sideways."

A second person proffers the name of the captain ("He's the one they took over from the Soarèses at Palma."). A third, that of the yacht's builder—in Gosport or Glasgow, naturally (many of these yachtsmen, who never call a yacht a yacht, but a cutter, sloop, yawl or schooner, sail under the British flag—a first-class label—since these boats are hired out by the English, who aren't interested in the summer).

When I speak of names, I'm not being precise. Usually it's only the first names which are involved. Judging by these initiates, you'd think that the world, far from including six continents, is made up of twenty-five Christian names which seem as reliably catalogued in their atlas brains as the commune of Suresnes in the cadastral survey.* At whatever place in the world—the smart world, of course—they happen to be (Formentor, Ischia, Venice, Barcelona), they always find someone to call by his Christian name, and always someone they know.

"Look, there's Patrick! And he's with Diana!"

"Guess where James is! I had a cable from him this morning." (They never send letters or postcards.) "With Tola and Sophie at Ibiza!"

And should you venture to ask one of them what he'll be doing in September:

"I'm going to Marie-Laure's. Jack"—not Jacques—"is

---

* *These Christian names can change every month, even every fortnight. But everyone knows that if there is talk of Françoise this week it can refer only to, let's say, Françoise Sagan.*

coming for us in the Carqueiras' yawl and we're going to pick up Alec at Corfu." For which read: three weeks in a villa in the south (Marie-Laure), a cruise on a shipowner's yacht which harbors a surrealist clientele and, to wind up, some shooting in Sologne from a little Louis XIII château.

To know the world as they do is difficult enough. To talk about it, or, rather, know what you must avoid saying about it, is more hazardous still. Suppose the conversation turns to Florence: *The Birth of Venus* is one of the things that must never be mentioned, along with the Duomo, the Piazza delle Signoria and the Medici tomb. San Miniato, since it is rather remote, may perhaps be referred to but only if absolutely necessary—and even then you run the risk of appearing as out of date as if you talked about Rockefeller Center on returning from New York.

As far as Florence and Venice are concerned, it's as much as these heroes can do to pronounce the names of the cities. To say "I adore the view from the Ponte Vecchio," for instance, marks you as completely hopeless. It shows that you haven't had the opportunity to go to Florence for the purpose of seeing something other than Florence. The best of all is to have gone to Florence or Venice without setting foot in the actual city. Thus, the revelation "I went to Fiesole to stay with Allegra Ruspoli di Ruspola. We never once went down—it was heaven!" isn't bad. A visit to the Uffizi can *just* be forgiven—but the Botticellis are out of the question. Better to say, "Up on the second floor, in a cabinet the curator opened for us, there's an absolutely stag-ger-ring little della Francesca."

It has to be admitted: these people have a genius not

only for finding "divine" places outside the city, but also for creating them if they don't exist. At Venice, for example, the height of chic is to go and dine on a practically inaccessible little island where you'll find the Fergusons, the Alonzos and the Dewatrins in the shelter of an old cloister converted into a barbecue restaurant. The very difficulty of access and the fact that you have to go there in a private launch are guarantees of its success. This is what the astute restaurant owner realized from the start; had he set up his barbecue in Venice itself, the lucrative clientèle, finding this far too simple, would have stayed away.

How long will this vogue last? It would be hard to say with any precision. From three months to two years. The departure of a headwaiter, the caprice of a film star, the defection of the Fergusons in favor of a pizzeria on San Francesco del Deserto (farther away still), will be all that's needed to make what had once been a ritual unfashionable. The aesthetes have an almost intuitive, at any rate immediate, knowledge of those places where it's smart to be seen and those which are passé. Even in Paris the wheel of fashion spins with such rapidity that people like us have a hard job keeping up with it. When the echoes of notoriety finally reach us, it's very often too late. It's no longer The Thing. Thérèse wanted to go to the Pentham Club, where it's all the rage to eat orange tart while listening to a guitarist (Hungarian) playing Bach. Every night at about eleven, so we were told, Sheila, one of the most ravishing mannequins in Paris (Irish), came and left her baby, wrapped up

190

in a shawl (Scottish), in the checkroom. Isn't that touching? It *was*, for Sheila goes there no more. Now she goes, it seems, to the Cisterna, where one enjoys *scampi* in tomato sauce while listening to a harpsichordist (Austrian) playing Lully.

5. A *hint of cruelty* (*conscious or unconscious*).

I was in a hairdressing salon on the Champs-Élysées, waiting for Thérèse to be finished. So I had plenty of leisure to listen to the grievances of an opulent lady who was in a state of the most agonizing uncertainty: she couldn't bring herself to decide whether to go to Cannes or Málaga in February and was confiding her perplexity to the manicurist, one of those smiling girls who see so many people of this kind suffering hideously every day.

"Which would you choose, Mireille?" the lady asked, with that tact which is the prerogative of people bowed down by wealth.

Mireille, thinking that Mme. Pontet-Massène was going to make her miss the six-thirty to Noisy-le-Sec, said, "Málaga." It made her think of grapes. Perhaps she'd take some home. Tomorrow.

"Yes, Málaga, to be sure," said the lady. "But the journey is so exhausting. The Spanish sleepers, my poor Mireille—you have no idea how hard they are! And then there's the coffee . . ."

"The coffee?" said the manicurist.

"Yes, I've never been able to stand Spanish coffee.

Whenever I go there I have to take a supply of Nescafé with me. The last time, I forgot it. It ruined everything for me. You have no idea!"

"Then Cannes. Madame Dalcide, whom I had this morning, has just come back from there. She had marvelous weather."

"That's what they always say when they come back from the south. Now, whenever I get there it's raining. Besides, nowadays the whole place is full of bricklayers—all Italians into the bargain. They're building too much. Anyway, when I think that I have a place sitting empty in Touraine . . ."

Mireille, dreaming of places sitting empty in Touraine, left Madame Pontet-Massène's plump hand dangling in suspense for a moment. Then she took up her orange stick again.

"It's dreadful how fat I've grown," wailed Mme. Pontet-Massène. "Just look at my hands!" She held up hands covered with cabochon emeralds and diamonds. "Look. Try to pull this ring off. Just try, Mireille. Try! Pull hard! Go on, pull, don't be afraid." Mireille tried to pull off a cabochon emerald—in vain, needless to say. "You see? If you wanted to get it, you'd have to cut off my finger!" A cackle of laughter.

Mireille would have been delighted to cut this finger off, and even one or two more. She pictured herself returning to Noisy-le-Sec with the cabochon. Such are the ideas that run in the heads of manicurists, but which are brought up short, except in the case of manicurists in Dostoevsky.

The lady sighed. "Anyway, we have March settled. We're going to Gstaad."

"Oh, Gstaad must be lovely, madame. Madame Rivière was there for Christmas. She seemed thrilled by it."

"Yes, it's a nice place. But think of it: a week to get acclimated, and then when one begins to feel at home— out! The hotel closes down on the twentieth. Incredible! 'Stay open till the thirtieth,' we told the manager. That's the trouble—there's one of those frightful gaps from the twentieth to the thirtieth. Lucien suggested the Canaries. But, oh, the Canaries—always the Canaries!"

It had probably never occurred to Mireille that there could be people fed up with the Canaries.

"This year, I don't know why, I felt drawn to Lebanon. But my husband pointed out that this isn't the right moment. It's a good thing he reminded me—I never notice what's going on in the world. I never read the papers. They're so dirty! The only impression they leave is on one's fingers." Cackle of laughter.

"Will you dip, madame?"

A young beauty entered the salon.

"That's the friend of Monsieur P.... You know, the champagne P...," whispered Mireille.

Mme. Pontet-Massène stared at the new client without favor.

"What do you suppose the age of that one can be? My God, how flat she is! I feel better off in *my* skin than I would in hers."

Base coat, polish. There! Finished. Cashier, please. How

193

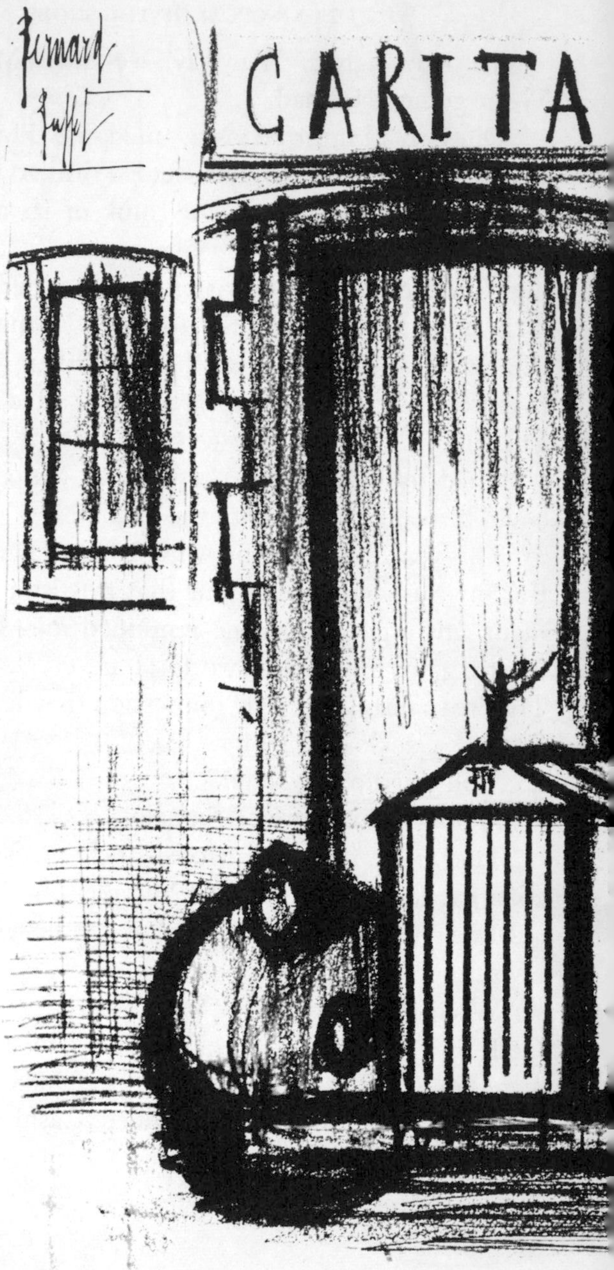
CARITA

much for Madame Pontet-Massène? Au revoir, Madame Pontet-Massène. Mireille accompanied the lady to the door. It was raining. Mme. Pontet-Massène complained of her rheumatism. The sight of Joseph, waiting cap in hand before the cream-and-black Bentley, comforted her.

"Ah, dear Joseph! He managed to find a parking place. In this weather, when one has to paddle about hunting for one's car . . . That's the way I caught my cold the other day. But you at least, Mireille, you have your health. That's the main thing in life. Well, my dear, we all have our crosses to bear, but there are many worse off than we!"

6. *A natural taste for abstract art.*

I confess it to my undying shame: Of all the spheres in which I am found wanting, that of abstract art must be one of the most vast. Before those multicolored rectangles, or even white on white, before those black areas with red eggs in the middle of them, those magmas which you can interpret, according to how you feel, as a landscape drowned under rain, a power station, a Paris street glimpsed at two hundred miles an hour or a seascape— all things which wring cries of admiration from the aesthetes ("Staggering." "Prodigious!" "What power!")—I remain dumb for lack of comprehension. A basic and heinous shortcoming, an indelible smirch of which I shall doubtless never correct myself and which must derive from my middle-class origins. Whenever I read a sentence or contemplate a picture, my first reaction is to want to understand it. I have always sought to understand. Is that perhaps being middle-class? I'm fairly sure it is, since all the experts to whom I unburdened myself of this pathological need to understand gave me clearly to understand (eventually) that this was curable.

This, then, is the frontier between art and myself. Like a traveler without a visa, I am put into quarantine by the immigration authorities of abstract art until cured of the desire to understand. In that hinterland whose gates I'll perhaps always be forbidden to pass through, I envy the countless hordes of citizens who immediately assimilate and savor words just as they come, brush strokes just as they're applied (when it isn't whole pots of paint), and who feel not the slightest need to understand. What am I saying! You *must not* understand. You can achieve the ideal state of euphoria only if you *don't* understand. The connoisseurs derive their pleasure from the very sources of my own discomfiture—from that chaos of colors around which my primitive eye flounders in dismay, despondency and dislocation. How could I help regarding them as immeasurably superior, since in front of two gray-and-green cubes their ecstasy is the equal of mine in front of a Michelangelo? Where I can see nothing, they see everything; where I get lost in utter perplexity, they perceive not only "a mad life force," but also "a handwriting," "a development"—even, as I saw printed on one of those invitations to an opening, "the memory of future developments from the past." And I have to leave them to their ethereal heights while I crawl about in my drawing class for beginners, hunting for a plumb line and a T square.

Only the other day I again had proof of this basic incapacity of mine when, in front of a sort of glutinous puddle which might just as well have been spilt ink, from the middle of which sprouted the leg of a Louis XV chair, I was rash enough to murmur, "But . . . what exactly does it mean?"

The reply wasn't long delayed. "Why do you want it to mean something? Doesn't it speak for itself?"

No doubt there exist things which speak for themselves in this way (those, for instance, of which the experts maintain, "It's a valid object"). I haven't the ears one needs to hear them, nor the eyes to admire them. And however hard I try to fathom the text on those invitations—"Helia Kazan invites you to accord your full and undivided attention to the lucid and positive expression of a new and depthless sensitivity which in Zulmo Picciolo governs the pictorial quest for an ecstatic and immediately communicable emotion"—my mind remains closed to its message.

God knows, I wish with all my heart I could respond to this type of art. I should so much like to gape with admiration before some lozenge containing a glittering orange eye, some gray sphere in which two black blobs are floating. But after thinking it over all I find to say in these cases is "It seems to me a child of seven could do just as well, perhaps even better."

An error. A fundamental error. Before no matter what square, circle or blob, never on any account mention the child-who-could-do-just-as-well, under pain of being immediately written off as a yokel, a provincial, a clod, a cave man—in short (for this term contains all these categories in one), middle-class. A hopelessly middle-class member of the middle-class, who will never understand anything about anything, especially when it's a question of a painter whose "massive noncolors, contrasting with his silken texture, melt into near-nothingness or potential somethingness."

I was dining a short while ago at the Daubersons' when I saw my neighbor suddenly go off into a trance in front of a slab bronze shaped like an irregular hexagon, perched high on a wooden pedestal. To her this mass of metal, this sort of helmet for a warrior with six noses, had not only a "desperate sensuality" but an "unbelievable dynamism." Being astonished at my total lack of reaction, she finally asked me what I did find pleasing in the way of sculpture. Timidly I hazarded Michelangelo, Donatello, Rodin. She stared at me as if I didn't yet have a telephone.

"Why not the Statue of Liberty?" she snapped.

I fully appreciate that the springs of emotion vary with each individual. I even know that nothing made Schopenhauer laugh so much as the sight of an equilateral triangle (it must have been his snobbish side). But I have to admit that, as compared with people who discern a desperate sensuality in hexagons and remain unmoved before the Venus de Milo, I have a very inferior intellect.

I no longer even need to appeal to experts to convince me that this old-fashioned need to understand is the indelible mark of my middle-classness. Thérèse is now the first to stigmatize it. Can abstract art have touched her with its grace? She has been conquered, not just by the abstract (you can no longer talk about "abstract art," any more than you can about existentialism, without appearing retrograde; the term is now reserved for Boeotians like me) but also by tachism. There's almost nothing she wouldn't be prepared to do to keep abreast of what is done and, above all, what is admired. She reads *L'Oeil* and other arty magazines and now swears by this little Picciolo, a young tachist who, she says, has a fantastic following and who certainly has no equal for wedging crushed eggshells between two layers of paint. That a woman normally so detached should have met her match in a tachist is something that, for me, is still beyond comprehension. But the fact remains that the two straightforward, simple mezzotints after Boucher which used to hang over our bed have given way to a sort of murky magma in which Thérèse sees, according to her mood or the time of day, an erupting volcano, a lighthouse in a stormy sea, the Moulin Rouge in rain or the inside of a sea urchin. (These, clearly, are extrapolations in which you could hardly indulge with a Boucher bathing girl, who, whatever her mood, obstinately remains a bathing girl.) Personally, I can see nothing in it whatsoever except, in the left corner, a little of that famous eggshell, this master chicken's trademark. Steeped in the vocabulary of the connoisseurs, Thérèse even goes so far as to talk of "explosive values." And should I, still spurred on by this accursed desire to understand, allow myself in turn to explode, she cries, "You're so middle-class!"

"Well, what else are we?"

"There's no need to advertise it!"

Actually, I don't advertise it. But if you really think about it, what would become of abstracts, tachists, lettrists, splashists and other tactilists if there were no honest middle class to buy them with their eyes shut? The honest middle class is always ready to revolt against the eccentricities of Picasso; they say he's pulling everyone's leg. But who, may I ask, made Picasso's fortune? The honest middle class in the first place.

7. *The general vocabulary.*

A thing is sublime, divine, remarkable, valid, prodigious,* staggering, stupefying, fascinating, positively sen-sa-tional, of a dazzling beauty, adorable, or else detestable, ghastly, insipid, unthinkable, inept, frightful, hideous, vile, mortally boring, annihilating. Between the peaks of rapture and the gulfs of savagery it seems there is no mean. Nowadays there's such an outlay of superlatives that the language has run dry and can't keep up with the demand. What did that moneyed lady say in the old days to express her condemnation of the martyrdom of millions of innocent men and women deported in sealed boxcars to the gas chambers? "It's frightful!" What does she say today because the creaking of a steel plate prevented her from getting a good

---

* *"It's pro-di-gious!" is said of almost anything, accompanied by a negative gesture of the hand, raised palm facing outward and waggled from left to right, by way of implying "And don't let anyone tell me the opposite."*

night's rest in her sleeping car? "It was frightful!" And if she feels a little warm in a night club, she'll say, "I nearly died!"

A crime is frightful, a woman is frightful, a hat is frightful. As for *sublime, divine* and *heaven,* they're preferably reserved for things in which the common run of mortals can discern nothing particularly remarkable: a bunch of anemones, some cufflinks, a little fishing village (provided it's unknown). Before a gas tank it's permissible to exclaim, "Simply exquisite!" But confronted with the Bay of Naples or the Parthenon, keep quiet—or else say it's very overdone.

One exception in this gallery of intoxication and castigation is the epithet *good.* To describe a man as "very intelligent" is banal; everyone is intelligent; "*very* intelligent" means "of an intelligence less stupid than another." *Good* is much better. I've heard a man go into ecstasies at an art-show opening, crying "Admirable!" before the first picture, "Marvelous!" before the second, "It's—spatial!" (worth remembering) before the third, and then, in front of the fourth, wishing to display a veritable peak of admiration, "Ah! Now, that's *good!*"

What characterizes the language of these people is its executive style. A book, a play, an artist, a man, all are executed in a twinkling, either upward or downward. Besides, it isn't necessary to have read, seen or heard. Regarding some famous actress, it's far less useful to discuss her acting or diction than to be able to reveal that she "lives alone in the country with four bulldogs." When talking of Picasso, only a mental deficient would dream of

saying, "I prefer his blue period to the rest." Much better
to be able to tell that the young woman who inspired so
many of his later canvases lives entirely on Turkish delight.
If the discussion tends to become prolonged, they never
hesitate to use certain formulas, devoid of all sense but full
of implied meaning. I've heard said of a novelist, "What
she does is quite remarkable, but—how shall I say it?—she
puts in too much, or not enough, you know what I mean?"
You haven't the right not to know. Most of the time all
this means nothing at all in practice, but it has form, and
the form is good. That's enough.

8. *A certain high-quality gibberish.*

All these people talk terribly quickly. They have so much
to say—and, if they haven't, so many ways of expressing
themselves in which to say nothing! There are moments
when the words pour in such a torrent from their lips that
—we must forgive them—they really haven't the time to
string their sentences together or branch out into details.
This is what justifies such short cuts as "You know what I
mean?" accompanied by an abrupt, nervous jerk of the
hand, a snap of the fingers or even a grimace. They absolve
the speaker of any superfluous explanation—at least if he's
talking to one of his circle—and enable him to get his
breath back before a further bowlful of words. There
are some—like M. de Stumpf-Quichelier—whose "what?,"
falsely interrogative since it assumes complete agreement
and sweeps aside any impulse to contradict, has become a

tic and is hung like an appendix on the end of every remark, sometimes together with a "no?": "That's really
overdoing it, what—no?," the whole being said with a
touch of banter, a hint of vulgarity, with the implication
"There's no question about it!"

No need to explain their thoughts more precisely. They
would have an embarrassment of choice should they try to,
they have such an infinity at their disposal—but why
should they? They might just as well say nothing at all.
They make themselves perfectly clear as it is, what? And
those who don't understand aren't worth the trouble of
having it explained to them.

The wildest unintelligibility, like the clearest diction, has
its special geniuses. I'd like to pay tribute here to the
Comte de Rieussec, who one evening in my presence gave
a dazzling demonstration of a verbal whirlwind. Rather shy
by nature, the Count is one of those men who give themselves courage by endless chatter. If he should have one or
two well-known talkers at his table, he sees to it that he
gets going before anyone else, knowing that if he gives the
others a head start he'll feel paralyzed and incapable of
taking off. That particular evening he had two strong op-
ponents to contend with, so from the moment he came in
he launched into a brilliant display. His range was phenomenal; from the Boer War and Fashoda to Brigitte
Bardot and intercontinental missiles, via the administration of the Opéra, the European Common Market, the
Rothschilds, shooting, the new restaurants, the devaluation of the franc, the latest prize-winning novel, Eden Roc

at Antibes and racing, nothing was left out. I can channel into this narrative hardly more than a drop of the torrent of words that poured out of him, with a faint clearing of the throat which in itself constituted a master touch, in the face of certain fellow diners less highly placed on the social ladder:

"Forgive my voice. I'm slightly hoarse tonight. I yelled my head off hunting today."

This "yelled my head off hunting," a stroke of genius, immediately placed its man for you—a keen rider to hounds, a well-known shot, a topnotch aristocrat of ancient lineage, but capable of descending to more plebeian levels by adorning his polished speech with a few apt expressions, and adept as no one else at mingling slang with the *Almanach de Gotha*. The supreme mark of the high-class snob who can permit himself to say, following an original epigram or a quotation from Plautus, "We split our sides laughing." But let us hear him speak for himself:

"My cousin the Duc d'Achabas, just as frightful as ever, by the way—it's true, he's nice but frightful, what?— was telling me yesterday as we drove through Puteaux— Incidentally, do you know what the inhabitants of Puteaux are called? Eh? Putéolians, yes, my dear, you can take it or leave it, and a Putéolienne—that's not at all, but not at all, what you might think. Funny, no? Yes, well, Achabas was telling me yesterday that it's all settled, the Houppaches and Vuilleaumes have patched it up, so much so that the younger Houppache girl, of the Solingen branch, you know Elaine, who is quite a catch, incidentally—yes, yes, very

much of a catch—is going to marry a nephew of Ghis-
laine's, a Weill d'Haricourt, but Vuilleaume through her
mother's mother. That will restore the fortunes of our bankers, who, by the way, are up to their ears in Venezuelan
oil—I heard that from my niece Ariane, who is a close
friend of President Juárez y Ortiz' daughter. Apart from
which, our bankers are getting along fine. I called on them
the other day at Louveciennes: Picassos and Matisses all
over the place, and even a Bielka—you know, that Pole
who's making such a name for himself. I must say he shows
extraordinary delicacy in his pastel tints, especially in his
landscapes, but when it comes to portraits he's a complete
mess. Apropos of money, another fellow who is not doing
too badly either is that old nut Cartebau-Sabray, who is
still dodging his creditors but has just inherited Cham-
bourcy from his late brother. Seventeen hundred acres of
forest and five farms—a godsend! It has put him back in
the saddle. So much so that the old scoundrel has just paid
over six million for a yearling at Deauville. You know the
family motto: 'Never say die!' Even so, we can't all carry
on like Onassis, what? Incidentally, Aristotle is damned
put out about his flags. At least that's what the Schneiders*
tell me. Since he can't use Panama or Liberia any longer
. . . However, this doesn't prevent him from being worth

---

* *Need I point out that the Count pronounced Schneider in the correct
way? Another delicate question concerns the pronunciation of great
names if one is anxious, like Thérèse, not to be immediately recognized
for what one is. Since she caused a lot of snickers when she referred to
the "Schnédairs," she makes a great effort to correctly pronounce Castel-
lane as "Cast-lan" and Broglie the same as Breuil.*

his weight in billions. Enough to outshine our dear Marquise. Whose son, by the way, has been catapulted up to the South Pacific Department. A fine recruit for the Quai d'Orsay! Notwithstanding, the arrant twerp has arranged to have himself elected a member of the Jockey Club. With only one more blackball he wouldn't have made it, but it was fixed. What with that and the fact that the Quai is sending him on a mission to Moscow . . . Incidentally, have you read about the new popgun the Russians have fired? It's enough to make you pop off a backfire of your own—a retroactive backfire, too, when you think that *behind* it all are German engineers. Hitler came within a hair's breadth . . . And to think that Mussolini would have been in on the party! Unthinkable! Anyway, that's all over now—but it could rise again. Fascism, at bottom, is a rush of Roman history to the brain. . . ."

Even if the Count didn't stop on this memorable line, I must, at any rate. I must add, however, that a little later a famous man with only one arm—a man wounded and decorated in the war—became the subject of this conversation, which wouldn't have been classic had it not left seven or eight absent eminent people strewn about the field. The Count, who, after his monologue, had allowed the others a chance to shoot, took up the war hero between his lips with as much disdain as ferocity.

"I've heard it said at the Jockey Club, but this with a big pinch of salt, eh?—I wouldn't like you to think . . . No, it's too *h*ideous—" he stressed the *h*—"but I've been assured it's true. Well, it appears that his arm— It isn't

209

very clear, but they say he cut off one of his fingers to avoid going to the front. Gangrene set in . . . they had to amputate. At least, I was guaranteed the truth of it. Not very pretty, what?"

12

THE ART OF MAKING
OTHERS TALK

Since I can never hope to achieve the voluble virtuosity of these inexhaustible talkers, I would like at least to be one of those conversation re-winders, who, while they usually remain silent themselves, are masters at the art of making others talk. Byron maintained that society falls into two groups: the bores and the bored. This is a fine but incomplete image; like all those which divide the world in two, there is always something left over. Midway between the bores and the bored, comfortably sitting back in semi-immobility, are to be found the re-winders who have the same effect on the talkers as on a clock: the minute their companion threatens to stop, they rekindle him with a key word.

Having had plenty of leisure to study the way in which these tenders that feed the fires of the talking locomotives function, I have attempted, following an irresisitible penchant of mine, to draw up a list of certain magic formulas which, while they permit you almost complete inertia, provide you with the means of holding your own in a conversation without making any.

A. BASIC EXCLAMATIONS WHICH ENABLE YOU, WITH A MINIMUM EXPENDITURE OF ENERGY, TO SHOW A PASSIONATE INTEREST IN YOUR COMPANION'S REVELATIONS AND ENCOURAGE HIM TO PURSUE THEM.

WELL, WELL!?

Jacques has a perpetually astonished air and a seeming thirst for further knowledge which act like a dope on talkers. His key words are *Well, well!?* at the same time exclamatory and interrogative; if this sounds a bit old-fashioned, it is nonetheless effective. A young man reveals to him that Mme. X is the mistress of Monsieur Z. A *Well, well!?* and everybody's in bed with each other. (In this particular circumstance, the *Well, well!?* is slightly ribald, Rabelaisian: "Quick, tell me all about it!" That is what is so interesting about this exclamation: it can be grave, comic, shrill, confidential. Its launching power, its impetus, remains the same.) Influenza, domestic worries, the international situation, holidays, prospects of matrimony—Jacques absorbs everything with an apparent voracity which puts his companion completely at ease.

AH!

You're telling me! Nothing could be more obvious! The rational use of the *Ah!* can produce excellent results. It is sufficient merely to follow up the *Ah!* with the speaker's last word.

Example: "*This summer my wife and I are planning to go to Greece.*"

"*Ah! Greece. . . .*"

This *Ah! Greece* . . . , spoken with a sigh, the eyes half closed as if you could see the Parthenon from your armchair, clearly indicates that you know everything the name of Greece implies—in other words, everything it can evoke for a genuine humanist or at least a man who has been through college.

OH, WELL . . .

If you don't know what to add or reply to what your companion has just said, it is not unprofitable to sigh, "*Oh, well. . . .*"

Example: "*And have you any idea how much more this mad whim of the government's going to cost us? A mere trifle of 500 millions!*"

"*Oh, well. . . .*"

A little on the feeble side, but quite philosophic. Implication: Anyway, there's nothing we can do about it; I fully share your views; how mad the world is! Can serve as a transition with almost anything.

OH HO!

Well! So *that's* it! Exclamation with sly undertones, recommended for use when dealing with alcoves or connecting bedrooms.

213

Example: "*Apparently he has a ravishing nurse who, so I'm told, doesn't confine herself to admitting the visitors. . . .*"

"*Oh ho!*"

No!

Although rather negative in appearance, the exclamatory *No!* permits many people to further the conversation in a positive way.

Example: "*And do you know how he began?* * *As a newspaper boy!*" †

"*No!*"

You are stupefied, it's not possible, you long to know more about it, it's one of the great surprises of the century.

No, really!?

What a shock! It's incredible!

Example: "*Do you know the Naudins? They were really the most devoted couple in the world. Well, now they're divorcing.*"

"*No, really!?*"

Wheeew!

A long-drawn-out whistle whereby you show your companion that the importance of what he has just

---

* *Even if you do know, you mustn't say so.*
† *The number of millionaires who began as newspaper boys has always amazed me.*

revealed hasn't passed you by: you are stunned.

Example: *"Do you know how much oil we could export if Hassi-Messaud was sensibly exploited? . . . No, just give me a figure, tell me what you think."*

Be careful not to say anything precise; if by any chance your figure was accurate, that would be that!

Leave it to the talker to announce with assurance: *"Two hundred million tons a year!"*

"Wheeew!"

B. EXPRESSIONS WHICH, ALTHOUGH MORE TIRING THAN THE FIRST KIND IN THAT THEY DEMAND A MORE FULLY DEVELOPED AWARENESS OF THE TOPIC IN HAND, PRODUCE EVEN MORE ENCOURAGING RESULTS.

BUT OF COURSE!

You are in complete sympathy with the talker, you feel exactly the same about it, you applaud his proposals enthusiastically. Anyone who thought otherwise would be a nitwit. You think as one.

Example: *"But seriously now, don't you think the first step that has to be taken is a complete reform of our system of social security from top to bottom?"*

"But of course!"

Another: *"Anyway, put yourself in my position.* Wouldn't you have reacted in the same way?"*

"But of course!"

---

* *If you had to put yourself in other people's positions every time they asked you to, you'd never find time to be in your own.*

OF COURSE NOT!

Used in the same sense as *But of course!* but in rather different circumstances. By *Of course not!* you not only accord the talker your complete agreement but also reinforce his feeling of being in the right.

Example: *"Do you think I'm going to let them put something like that over on me?"*

"Of course not!"

Implication: With someone of your ability, it would be unthinkable! You've seen right through them. What do they take you for?

HOW TRUE!

The invigorating effect of these two words, which may be increased to three (*How very true!*), cannot be overestimated. They fill the speaker with lawful pride and incite him to carry on while you sit back.

Example: *"In France it isn't the government which governs but the civil service!"*

"How true!"

Variations such as *Exactly!* produced at suitable moments in the manner of a fencer crying *"Touché!"* have the same tonic effect on the talker and spur him on for at least another ten minutes. As one of the master keys of the conversation-winder, it puts the speaker completely at his ease. Implication: Nothing as profound has been said in the world for several weeks.

Example: *"People complain about the youth to-*

day. They say they're worse than ever before. But the truth is, and I don't hesitate to say so, it's the parents who ought to be brought into court."

"Exactly!"

AS YOU YOURSELF POINTED OUT . . .

For more highly developed conversation-winders-by-interruption. Although this phrase demands greater effort than those preceding examples, it is always very rewarding. It may be that, after having gotten through a good part of the evening with *Well, well!?, But of course!* and a few *Wheeews!,* Jacques realizes that his talker is at the end of his tether and is about to start asking him personal questions. It is now that he displays a kind of genius. Far from racking his brains in search of a new topic, he rummages among the copious material which the speaker has just dumped in the drawing room and repeats word for word one of these opinions, preceded by the formula *As you yourself just pointed out* . . . The talker is enchanted to see himself done such justice in public. Sometimes—when he feels in especially good form— Jacques even beckons to some of the other guests and brings them in as witnesses:

"As our friend Rochelard just pointed out, it's absolutely crazy for the underdeveloped countries . . ." (or Morocco, or the women's vote). It's not at all certain that Rochelard ever mentioned the underdeveloped countries (or Morocco, or the women's vote),

at least in the terms employed by Jacques. No matter. The effect of this phrase is miraculous: it puts the speaker into such a state of mental intoxication that you can, without any difficulty, make him say the opposite of what he was saying before. He will never contradict you.

AND THEN?

Of all the ways of holding your own in a conversation without conversing, one of the best is undoubtedly the *And then?*

One evening I saw a little man who looked utterly insignificant wriggling in the clutches of a conversational Hercules who had pinned him in a corner of the ring with a firm grip on the international situation. The little man had set the machine going by means of a "What's it all leading up to?" whereupon Hercules strode into the White House and settled relations with the U.S.A.

That wasn't enough for the little man, who immediately asked, "*And then?*"

Acknowledging the blow, the man of the hour took a transpolar plane, landed at Moscow, went into conference and insured peaceful co-existence.

"*And then?*" said the insatiable little man. "*What do you do about China in all this?*"

The champion made a huge parcel of it and got quite out of breath tying it up; he was reeling when, at 11:30 P.M., a new and mocking "*And then?*" sent him bounding off into the Pacific. A few seconds later his wife threw in the sponge: "We must be going, darling. You can't argue all night with this gentleman."

13

THE KEYS
OF FORTUNE

I'M NOBODY's fool over a sou, but over millions I become a complete idiot.

I've lost any lingering doubts as to this since Providence brought a certain amount of money within my reach.

It isn't hard to see why. If you have only a sou, nobody rushes to tell you what you should do with it. Who cares whether you keep it or throw it out the window? When, on the other hand, chance brings millions of francs tumbling down about you,* you are plagued by people whose one occupation seems to be looking out for new millionaires so that they can lavish advice on them and urge them to do something with their money.

Mankind is far less selfish than it is generally made out to be; the proof of this is that people seem infinitely more preoccupied by others' wealth than by their own. Doesn't this impulse stem from the most praiseworthy of intentions? It's for my own good, in short, that they display such anxiety; having never had any money come my way before,

---

* Here again, I am reckoning in old francs.

I would commit endless acts of folly if left on my own. The more so since mine is a special case. If some citizen goes off under cover to the Pavillon de Flore to draw his one-tenth share of the first prize in a government lottery, he's not obliged to account for it to anyone. But in my case I feel spied on every moment of the day. Without feeling they are meddling in what is no concern of theirs, people unfailingly want to know what I'm going to do with all this money.

Now I can view the situation rather more objectively. Having profited from the sage counsel bestowed on me by countless well-meaning advisers, I'm happily in a position to see the problem as a whole and to confer the benefits of my experience on others. In fact, my experience seems to me wide enough to permit me to draw the conclusion that there are five ways of making a fortune:

1. By putting your money in the bank.
2. By buying stocks and bonds.
3. By buying gold.
4. By buying paintings.
5. By buying land.

When you possess these five keys to fortune, you feel like a different man. Judging that there is no sense in keeping them to myself, I'm pleased to list them here. By the same token, I feel I have no right to withhold something else more disturbing: namely, that at the same time there exist five ways of losing everything you have—and even more:

1. By putting your money in the bank.
2. By buying stocks and bonds.

222

3. By buying gold.
4. By buying paintings.
5. By buying land.*

1. THE SAVINGS BANK

In order to preserve the money they have, the first idea which strikes simple souls, and even souls less simple, is to put it aside. However, the first advice they receive from the experts is not to keep it. How can these two tendencies be reconciled?

Having been raised in the cult of Benjamin Franklin, Jacques Laffitte and all those sacred monsters whom our early schoolbooks revealed to us as having got their start in life by saving up their money penny by penny, I myself have known wild bouts of saving during which I put by everything that came my way, from old bits of string to burned-out light bulbs. I have always been haunted by the example of Jacques Laffitte, who began his prodigious career as a financier by taking a pin he had picked up in the street to a bank. Yet something which occurred in the now distant past showed me that honesty doesn't always pay so well. It was when, in my thirteenth year, I took a purse I had found to the local police station—and got myself called a sneakthief, a pickpocket and a little blackguard. Because it was empty, I was accused of having extracted the money it must have contained. The actual thief was arrested three

---

* A *possible variation is the horses* (*see p. 233*).

days later, but I have never picked up anything in the street again.

Besides, things have changed very much since the days of Jacques Laffitte. Things or money. I'd like to know what sort of welcome banks like the Société Générale or the Crédit Lyonnais would give today to the pedestrian who took it into his head to bring in a trombone or a pin he had picked up outside one of their branches. And then, whereas in the old days one could put by twenty million francs without incurring general disapproval, just try today doing the same thing with a million without being made to feel guilty!

I shall long remember the look of commiseration given me by a financial expert when, in reply to his question "Well, what are you going to do with all that money?," I confided, "I'm going to put it aside." It was all too clear that in his eyes I was an innocent—or mad. There and then he demonstrated to me that nothing could be more dangerous. One might just as well keep a ton of nitroglycerine or a radioactive element in one's house. Thus this money which Providence had so long delayed placing in my hands, this manna fallen from heaven, must at all costs be got rid of as quickly as possible under pain of seeing it melt away like a block of ice. In keeping it by me I was inviting it to undergo the fate of the ten little Indians with each successive devaluation. I must put it to some use without further delay, transform it, buy no matter what so long as it was something—shares, for instance.

"Sound equities, of course," the expert told me. "Some-

THE KEYS OF FORTUNE

thing solid. They do exist. All you need is a sound adviser. . . ."

2. STOCKS AND BONDS

Advised I was.* To such an extent and by so many
people that, if I had any advice to give today, it would be
to advise against advisers.

The newcomer who tries his hand at the stock market
very soon learns a few basic principles which are the ABC
of a financial career. Principles of the greatest simplicity,
sometimes couched in an exquisite fashion, even in verse.
Such as the first one: "Buy when the cannon fire begins.
Sell to the sound of violins." Is that not as explicit as it is
charming?

So I waited for cannon to thunder in some part of the
world in order to buy. I didn't have long to wait. But this
cannon fire, if not exactly a laughing matter, didn't prove
very serious. Nowadays they open fire for a yea or a nay—
sometimes for both—and, contrary to what used to happen
fifty years ago, a general conflagration doesn't automatically
ensue. This time the cannon overshot the mark, according
to one of those hallowed expressions so dear to our tongue

---

* People often say to me, "You, being an actuary, must know about figures." Yes, in theory. I am an adept at calculating pension scales, dividends, returns. But as for divining the psychological factors which determine the rise or fall of shares on the stock exchange, that's none of my
business. It's not enough to be an accountant to avoid having figures play
dirty tricks on you, any more than it's enough to be a banker never to go
bankrupt.

which mean exactly the opposite of what you would think. (When I recall that we could say that the Suez campaign "fell short" and that it "overshot the mark," and that these both mean the same thing, I pity foreigners.) On that day, then, the Bourse never stirred. Three weeks later, the cannon thundered in earnest somewhere in Africa and my beautiful shares fell like a meteor.

As far as violins go, I am keeping my ears open, of course, but up to now I haven't heard anything very beguiling. Our age, it must be conceded, is not particularly given to playing the violin. One day, however, thinking I could just detect a few encouraging strains, I decided to sell. It was too soon.

The expert consoled me with another of those well-known axioms: "Never forget that Rothschild made his fortune by selling too soon." The idea of being likened to a Rothschild momentarily gave me a pleasant feeling of comfort and security, but these are fleeting sensations which don't leave much behind once they have died away. After having reminded me that by and large one must do as others do, this skilled practitioner concluded, "You're in too much of a hurry. Too much of a hurry to buy, too much of a hurry to sell. Your shares? Keep them! You must sit on them and put them out of your mind. At the Bourse, only one thing really counts—your long-term investments."

The Bourse, then, is one of those places where they tell you that only one thing really counts. Unfortunately, it is never the same thing. As always! God knows how many times I've heard "Only one thing really counts—children," when it isn't good health, a good wife, a good bed, a good cook or country life. On the stock market, the only thing that really counts for some is long-term investments, for others speculation in oil, for still others holdings in gold mines. As all the experts are highly intelligent men, it cannot be doubted that each one of them is right. That is why, just as it is said to be a good thing to have a good wife, good children and good health, so it is a good thing to own oil, chemical products and gold mines.

"Why, then," one of my advisers asked me, "don't you take up a little Roquefort cheese? Have you got any Roquefort?"

No, I had to confess, I had never taken any Roquefort at the Bourse.

The specialist glanced down the list of my holdings. "You seem rather overloaded with oils," he told me, as if I had a liverish tongue. "You could even reduce a bit in copper. We might job some off and put you into cement. What with that and Roquefort your bread will be buttered on both sides."*

When I retorted that this step would be to my detriment, since copper had fallen, my expert taught me another axiom:

"There are times when one must know how to cut one's

---

* Butter, in France, is closely associated with wealth ("He buttered his bread"—when it isn't "his spinach"—"With that you'd get no more dividends than butter on a skewer," "At the price butter is!," etc.). Certain experts even consume so much of it in their vocabulary that on leaving them I get the feeling of having been buttered up.

losses. It's hard, I know, but what must be must be!"

So I had my losses cut—and the Bourse continued to function. Cement appealed to me. There was something reassuring about it. Besides, wasn't it wonderful to be able to convert my oils and copper into cement and Roquefort by a simple telephone call? I took a little of both. I already felt myself better equipped. And on that account I respected the sempiternal axiom: "Never put all your eggs into one basket."*

With my investments thus organized, I should, as the expert told me, have "sat on them" and put them out of my mind. I can't, therefore, be the right man to have investments. I like things to keep moving, and in the right direction. At the end of a few weeks the passion for giving orders seized me again. Perhaps simply on account of that obscure shiver of delight I get when I say to the telephone, "Sell!" I had often dreamed of being one of those magnates who, smitten with a hunch about cotton, telephone in their pajamas from a palace in California and thereby provoke a boom in Sydney or a crash on Wall Street while they are still in their baths. I have fulfilled this dream—but in my own way. Having made up my mind to sell some holding which is too stationary for my liking, all I have to do is call up my broker and the stock market is seized with panic; prices fall, and on that day shares sell at the lowest figure ever reached. And if, by chance, I happen on certain shares that look promising and decide to acquire some, a telephone call is all that's required for these shares

---

* Again this dairy connotation!

(whom nobody ever bothered about before) to shoot up, from the very opening of the morning's trade, higher than they have been marked for the past six months. (Sometimes, even, wishing to toy with fate in secret, I say to myself, "Let's pretend I'm buying today. No one else will know. We'll see what happens!" Well, on that day the market is bad; I would have been able to buy in fact under the most favorable circumstances. But if I really do buy the next day, these same shares go skyrocketing again.) That mysterious forces act against me and seem to warn the market, "Stop him from buying at all costs!" I do not doubt. But, after having believed that I exercised a personal influence on the Bourse, I have since had to face the fact that there was nothing very extraordinary about my case. Stockbrokers are categorical on this point: every one of them counts among his clients two or three individuals like me who always arrive too late or too early. They have just as good a nose as anyone else, but it's stuck on upside down. I know one broker who amassed a fortune within two years by meticulously executing on his own account the very opposite of the orders he executed for a client. And it's still going on, for this type of perverseness can never be discouraged.

Finally I went back to my first counselor, the man of investments. I was determined now to sit on them, but wanted to know for precisely how long.

He waved his hand evasively. "Ten years, twenty . . . What with successive devaluations, you're certain to make a profit."

To remain sitting on my investments for twenty years seemed beyond my powers. Moreover, even at the end of twenty years would I sell? One must never sell low. One must never be in a hurry to sell high. So when? Never. That is how one becomes rich. "One is rich when one lives on the income from one's income."

These shares were burning my fingers. In the end I sold them all—at a loss. And I fell back on the most sensible solution:

3. GOLD

To tell the truth, I had thought about gold even before I had any money. One of my uncles, an uncle of principles if ever there was one, used to maintain, like a number of speculators, "One should always have a little gold." (One feels that the people who say this have a great deal more.) "Later on, if you make any money," he instructed me, "buy gold. Put it in a canvas bag, sew it up, shove it under your shirts and keep it. Your gold is like your dog: it must follow you everywhere. You'll see, someday there'll be fireworks somewhere or other and your gold will go up in value. When that moment comes, you'll say, 'My uncle was right.'" This uncle, who took advantage of the leisure that retirement brought him to cultivate his investments, held Luzenac Talc in particular veneration. "I got them at three seventeen. Now they're standing at seventeen thousand. I'm always being urged to sell. But I'm hanging on to them. I'll hang on to them till I die, and when I've finally rolled up my umbrella my heirs will be amazed at what they'll find in my wallet." My uncle died liberally sprinkled with talc, and his children lived happily ever after.

It was thinking of him that finally gave me the idea of buying gold. To tell the truth, here again I found no lack of advisers.

"Go in for gold!" my expert had told me. "With that you're well covered. Soon you'll be staggered at the results."

Shortly after, I went back to him, staggered beyond words. He seemed radiant.

"Well now," he said, "aren't you happy?"

"Happy? How could I be happy to lose five hundred thousand francs?"*

"You've lost, I agree. But what a feeling of security!"

"?"

"Why, yes, of course. If gold goes down, it shows that things are all right. The country is in a healthy financial state; there's no danger of war; you can sit back and relax. Isn't that worth five hundred thousand francs?"

"All the same, if I had made them instead of losing them—"

"That would be proof that things were going badly, that we were on the verge of bankruptcy, war or revolution. Who knows? You might even be in prison!"

Lost for a moment in this gloomy prospect, I felt cheered by the professional's arguments. By the time I reached home, I had recovered my spirits. The wonderful

---

* *Old ones.*

power of gold. Had I squandered five hundred thousand francs at the races or roulette, I'd have been eaten up with remorse, like those in the *leçons de choses*. But to court ruin by buying gold was truly the most sober-minded way of making a fool of oneself (my old uncle hadn't foreseen that!).

So it was with a smile that I said to Thérèse, "Have you seen? Gold is dropping. It's wonderful!"

And when she asked me if I was feeling all right, I revealed to her my extraordinary sense of security. This didn't appear to convince her.

"I'm tired," she snapped, "of you and your sovereigns!" (She had previously said "our.").

I examined one of the pretty little coins, which had been bought as much with a view to a mink coat as to appendicitis, but whose power seemed to be declining toward rabbit and tonsils. Britannia, indifferent to her waning value, continued to rule the waves, while St. George still pursued his activities with his lance.

"It's very simple. All you had to do was sell them at the right time."

Very simple, obviously. But in order for there to be people who can sell at the right time, there naturally have to be others like me who buy at the wrong time.

"With the five hundred thousand francs you've lost we might have bought . . ."

There followed an avalanche of basic necessities and even ultimate luxuries: clothes for the children, a washing machine, a skiing outfit, not to mention several dresses. I could have bought the whole world with five hundred thousand francs. It's enough to make one really believe that the prime condition for putting a sum of money to judicious account is not to part with it.

My adventures with gold having lasted long enough, I decided to retire from the Bourse.

In the meantime, it's true, there had been an interlude. . . .

INTERLUDE: RACING

If I come to talk about the Course after the Bourse, this is not out of any desire to follow alphabetical order, since actually these two sources of ruin or profit differ by only one letter. I'm beginning to wonder if I'm not going through a period of my life in which I make a mess of everything I touch, the last thing I made a mess of after the Bourse being, precisely, that superb mechanism called the race horse.

Among the many ideas which, since the contest, have entered my mind and unhappily lodged there, there came to me the one of buying a thoroughbred. This dream, tenderly cherished in the obscurity of my former state (one has marvelous dreams only when they're based on a mediocre reality), the manna of my millions enabled me to bring true. Following the advice of an enlightened friend who had warned me, "In racing, my friend, you simply have to travel first class," I purchased a two-year-old, all the more costly because he had just won. Did he find the price inadequate? Or did he take an instant dislike to his new owner's looks when I went to inspect him at Maisons-Laffitte? From the first moment he bore my colors, he never again put one hoof in front of the other, as they say in the jargon of the turf.

Oh how wonderful it is, the day when you go to admire the horse in his stall for the first time! How gleaming his chestnut coat! How noble his stance! The stable boy fondly talks to him.

"This one can really go!" the boy confides to you.

Can there then be thoroughbreds that don't?

"And . . . is he entered for any big events?"

"All of them, monsieur. Look . . ."

You are handed the sheet with the magical names: Prix Lupin, the Derby, the Jockey Club, the Ascot Gold Cup. O new owner, make the most of this moment when your horse hurtles to victory before the Queen of England, and when you see yourself being congratulated in the Royal Enclosure! The horse is entered, it's true, but so are eight out of every ten thoroughbreds from birth, and at the time when your dream is whizzing him past the post, six hundred beasts are still engaged in the race. There will be only twenty of them left when they actually start. Longchamp, Chantilly, Epsom—glorious meetings where your colors will shine only on the race track of your dreams.

"We're running at Tremblay tomorrow," the trainer suddenly announced to me one day by telephone.

Strange. "Above all, don't be impatient," I had been

told. "You must pick a nice little track that just suits you."
Now it appeared that this horse, whose calm temperament
had been so widely extolled, was acting up in his stall; he
must be raced. He will race. He is racing. But all the same,
it's odd: I had been informed that this scion of Attis ran
well only over seven furlongs. Now he's to race over a mile
and a half. However, seeing the name of Blot printed on
the race card between those of the Aga Khan and M. Mar-
cel Boussac was agreeably titillating. And my heart beat
fast when, for the first time in my life, I went into the
parade ring to give the jockey my instructions (based, of
course, on my trainer's). For once I'm in the "big time"—
with those whom only yesterday I gazed at from the other
side of the white railings, engulfed in that anonymous
throng which inhales the odor of the owners from afar and
strains to overhear their precious comments. I have to keep
a strong grip on myself not to stare back at all those faces
staring at me, among which I almost find myself searching
for my own, my old face, to see what effect I'm having on
myself. I feel at once anxious and in seventh heaven. Two
feet away, a Rothschild. A little farther off, Baron de
Waldner. And I, Blot . . . I'd like to have time stand
still, the race held up, the spell not broken. What if my
horse comes in last?"

The jockey touched his cap when he was introduced to
me.

"Good afternoon, Gravelot!" I said in a tone I should
have liked to sound offhand but whose artificial familiarity
brought me back memories of the "Good day, friend!"

addressed by so many middle-class vacationers to peasants in the summers of my youth.

With a smile, Gravelot replied, "Afternoon, M'sieur Blot." Then he listened to the trainer's instructions:

"Are you sure you've got it? Put him into his stride and don't ask anything more of him until after you get into the straight. Treat him gently."

Seeing the horse pass by, led by his stable boy, I said, "He looks well!"—for the sake of something to say.

"He's a good horse," remarked the trainer, "and he's going to run a good race. But his *raie de misère** is—well, it does sort of stand out."

With horses, it's unusual if there isn't some small thing that isn't quite right, such as a *raie de misère*, sore hocks or bucked shins—always this mania for technical terms in which the specialists love to drown the layman. You have to look as if you understand. To achieve which, I acted as if I knew where this *raie de misère* was.

"Yes," I agreed, "it *is* a little prominent."

The trainer added no more. Had he not mentioned it first, and had I said, "It seems to me that his *raie de misère* sticks out too much," he would have stared at me in amazement, as if I were saying God knows what. Where have I had this same feeling of embarrassment before? I know: talking to garagemen.

The horses cantered down to the starting point. I took my place in the members' stand. On the way there, a stranger accosted me.

---

* *raie de misère*—a streak of bad luck.

"I saw you on television, M'sieur Blot. Is it safe to put something on you?" I sketched an evasive gesture. The man must have interpreted this as a reply in the affirmative, for he turned to a crony and told him, "It's all right—I got the word! He didn't want to come out and say it, but it's safe. Don't worry, he's out to win today!"

Came the start. Not only was "I" not left at the post, but I had the added satisfaction of seeing my colors leading the field. The loudspeaker even mentioned the name of my horse once. Once! It was to be the last time. At the turn he was swallowed up by the main bunch. By the end, I was an also ran (for which read "nowhere").

"He can't act on a right turn," concluded the trainer.

Two weeks later, a second race at another track, this one with bends to the left. Same result. Would this foal, which could act neither clockwise nor counterclockwise, act up only in his stall? No. "He doesn't give the same performance on the track as he does at morning exercise," explained the trainer. I thus learned that there are horses who don't care to race after lunch. Now, even if I've occasionally heard of races being held at night, there do not exist any morning meetings to my knowledge. The trouble is, this susceptible animal doesn't like crowds.

"He gets stage fright, like an actor," I was informed.

But it must also be noted that he doesn't like solitude either. He takes a great delight in the company of females. Too much, even: when racing he tends to stay behind them. That happens, it appears. Most vexing. Should he be gelded?

"Your little horse would do very well over obstacles," declares the trainer.

This "little" has an odd ring in my ears. It's a far cry from the horse who could really go. And never before has there been any question either of little or of fences.

It's only fair to add that my horse doesn't like a wet track, but that his delicate hoofs react badly to hard ground; that he likes to go out in front, but that a complete race spent in front threatens to deprive him of the necessary stamina for the final spurt; lastly, that he has to have a jockey strong enough to keep him well balanced and hold him back, but at the same time restrained enough to avoid use of the whip (always to be discouraged with sensitive spirits).

One finds these things out in time—but, as with second-hand cars advertised as being "as good as new," one finds them out later.

And what if I asked the jockey's advice? He, for one, must know what stuff this animal is made of.

"Between ourselves, what do you really think of him?"

A moment's hesitation, then: "Well, just between you and me—I wouldn't want to give any offense, M'sieur Blot, but he's not much of a horse."

Affronted, I retorted, "But the trainer told me . . ."

"Oh, well, if you like to believe what trainers tell you!"

With the utmost caution, I passed on the jockey's opinion to the trainer.

"Oh, well, if you like to believe the things jockeys tell you!"

238

All in all, there's only one point on which trainers and jockeys agree, and that is that owners know nothing.

4. PAINTINGS

Left to myself, I might have escaped. With Thérèse, no. So I began to buy abstract paintings. In spite of myself, without conviction, even with reticence. But I had to give in. Between Thérèse and me wealth has established certain conventions: she never says anything about my horse; I never cavil at her pictures. Nevertheless, I have my reasons for being reticent, not only over abstract art but over painting in general.

A long time ago now, my parents' estate was reduced to dust by a cavalry charge. At first glance there would have been no relation of cause and effect in that, had this devastating cavalry charge not been signed "Meissonier." I couldn't exactly say in what circumstances this Meissonier of fifteen horses made its entry into the family in about 1860. What I do know is that, after having caused my great-grandfather to be held in high esteem by connoisseurs, the celebrated canvas held my forebears in thrall for nearly a century.

The master's horses, objects of the most costly insurance, restorations and rebacking, have received more care and attention than any biped in the family. In order that this treasure should not be harmed by any sunlight, the salon in which it occupied the place of honor was kept in a permanent penumbra which plunged my grandmother into melancholia. In summer my grandfather himself would take the picture to be stored in the Place de l'Opéra, in a safe in the Société Générale bank.

When the 1914 war broke out, the Meissonier—which had been exhibited with honor at the 1887 Salon and was then valued at twenty million francs—left for Bordeaux before anyone else, given over to the care of a trusted agent, an usher in the Chamber of Deputies. It was to end the war in a closet at Brive, in the house of an uncle. Although the family had been through some hard times, the idea of selling its Meissonier would have struck it as sacrilegious.

"One doesn't sell the French Army," my grandfather used to say.

When he died, too late to have been able to dispose of the picture at its top price, too soon for us to have lost our Meissonieresque illusions, the famous artist's reputation had considerably declined. But at the time of the Great Divide—two branches of Blots were disputing the inheritance—the Meissonier still weighed so heavily in the scales that, in order to secure it, my parents renounced all the furniture, silver and table linen. The day when this accursed picture finally took its place among us—it was the Dada period—its price had come plunging down.

"Don't you worry," a dealer told my father. "It will go up again someday."

When the 1929 crash came, my father, held back by some strange, atavistic respect, still hadn't made up his mind to sell. One doesn't easily shake off the idea that a picture has been worth twenty million, to accept in exchange the fact that it is now worth only one. For this reason the few objects of value left to us were allowed to go at rock-bottom prices while Meissonier's horses continued to gallop into the dining room, the sole witnesses of our meager repasts—from which horse was not always absent.

When, in my turn, I found myself the owner of this tenacious work of art, it was worth fifty thousand francs, the price of one horse for slaughter.

"Besides," an expert auctioneer told me, "one has to find people who aren't afraid. Cavalry doesn't go over so well nowadays. It was all right in its time. But people don't want it any more."

It! My ancestors would have turned in their graves. Moreover, I had too great a respect for the family and the Army to compromise at fifty thousand.

So I kept the picture. But some time ago Thérèse, who, without being especially drawn to cavalry charges, had never displayed any real hostility toward this one, announced to me quite categorically that she wanted no more of it. Doubtless because some snob had told her that Meissonier puts one beyond the pale.

"Those soldiers," she declared, "get me down."

In the end, I put the Meissonier in the attic. It had never risen so high in fifty years.

Sometimes I go up and look at it. It wasn't so badly painted, after all. Besides, it was done at a time when, in order to represent a cavalry charge, they didn't hesitate to put in horses (this strictly between ourselves, of course—I don't want to get myself laughed at). In truth, we're so far from Meissonier today that one could almost wonder if he painted on the same planet.

Who knows? Someday a reaction may set in against abstract art. Who can tell if Meissonier won't come back just as he went out—at a gallop?

Meanwhile, you can understand why I'm suspicious, so far as painting goes. One can't have the flair everyone else has—and I say "everyone" advisedly, for in all the time I've been invited out by people whose walls are hung with Gauguins, Matisses or Modiglianis, I've never met anyone who told me, "I had to pay a fantastic price for that!"

It's not surprising that so many artists, even the most expensive ones, die in poverty. Suppose my eye is caught by a Boldini in one of these connoisseurs' houses. "Aha! So you're admiring my little Boldini?" he says with a gleaming eye. "I picked it up in the flea market—you'll never guess for how much. Eight hundred francs!"

My flair, in its way, must be exceptional. Lacking that of the multitude, I could never hope to make a fortune out of pictures, even under the aegis of Thérèse. Financially speaking, this forms only a sideline for me. There are happily more solid things, like:

5. REAL ESTATE

Why didn't it occur to me before? And yet it wasn't for want of advice received. Hardly a day passed without people weighing me down with instances of friends who had waxed rich thanks to real estate.

"X bought five hundred acres of land in Sologne for five million in 1938. And do you know how much they offered him for it in 'fifty-eight? Twenty-four million!"

Land! Here's another one of the panaceas of which people tell you, "It's the only thing that really counts!" I sometimes wonder if there's anything in the world which doesn't really count. "It's solid, it's there, it's safe. And besides, you have something that belongs to you. Oh, to be able to feel the earth under your feet and say to yourself, 'This is mine!'—you don't know how wonderful it is."

On this globe where we are in transit and do not belong even to ourselves, people practically never sing the praises of anything except eternal values and possessions.

In the light of the foregoing, the reader will naturally be led to believe that I met with no success in real estate either. There are so many ways of ruining yourself over land, however little you interfere with it in an endeavor to grow something or to embark on the breeding of beavers. But no. I don't regret the little patch of earth I have bought and on which, relieving me of any impulse toward rash and ill-considered ventures, my predecessors had had a small shack built. I can say with truth that, of all the things I've bought as a result of the contest, this is the only one I haven't yet tried to sell again.

14

THIS DEAR
TRANSPARENCY

Wно still talks about the contest?

The last time the subject cropped up, I would have been just as happy if the whole thing had been dropped. A certain M. Gruchot, who had been hot on my heels with a 2.05, went so far as to claim the first prize through the medium of a lawyer, on the grounds that my position as an actuary had allowed me to procure a knowledge of statistics inaccessible to the ordinary run of mortals. In the end, the matter was never brought to court. But doubts had been sown in the public mind. Since a scandal had simultaneously broken out in the United States over television quiz shows, gossip rapidly began spreading to the effect that the contest had been rigged. Although these insinuations had absolutely no basis in fact, they soon raised the wind of slander, which is always ready to blow. And it needed no more than this for the mail to bring me anonymous letters whose authors never failed to point out that they had seen through me from the start. What matter if my good faith is patently obvious? In the eyes of some

I'll always appear a hoaxer. Even at the office I've over-heard various unpleasant remarks.

At my approach, people start to whisper. "It has always amazed me . . ." "I used to say to myself he's not the type." "There's something fishy about it, mark my words!"

For me, from that moment on, Providence became Fatality. I know these fluctuations of fortune—I know them at least on my own small scale. For a long time past, I've been in the habit of classifying my days as red or green ones. If I cut myself shaving in the morning, if the first telephone number I dial is busy, if the concierge delays me on the stairs, if the man at the newspaper kiosk tells me he has just sold his last copy, if out of the various traffic lanes I pick the one that's moving the slowest—then I know my day will be red. As an actuary, I have certain qualms about admitting this, but, by dint of spending all my time calculating probabilities, I do the same for every-thing, whether it be my chances of getting through the gate in the Métro before it automatically shuts at the train's approach, or of seeing the car just in front of me stop at the next gas station before I do.* This may seem childish, but it isn't always futile; experience has taught me that sixty-nine times out of a hundred, instead of pulling in toward the curb, the cyclist you're preparing to pass will swing out into the middle of the road.

From the moment when this Gruchot put in his claim, I understood that I was, so to speak, in the red. On every ac-

* Not to mention the games of poker dice I secretly play against myself, reckoning from the way the dice fall the sort of luck I'll have that day.

count. I had calculated that there was one chance in sixty-six billion that one of those birthday greeting cards which had been my idea would arrive at the insured's domicile on the day of his decease. Well, the utterly improbable eventuality occurred. And the family didn't fail to write to the president-director general expressing their astonishment at so awkward a coincidence. Overnight, the dispatch of birthday cards was suspended. Already impaired by the false scandal of the contest, my credit suffered a further loss.

"Things will settle down in time," Barnage told me with a protective air. "Everyone has been talking about you too much, my dear Blot. You're going to miss the days when you lived in obscurity. Meanwhile, what would you say to a little tour of inspection in Auvergne? These tours have their charms. But you know for yourself, you've been on them before. There's an agent near Saint-Flour who . . ."

"Everything passes with time."

I was now being asked to bury myself once again in the oblivion out of which Providence had lifted me.

When the bough breaks, the cradle will fall . . .

I have come back from a journey into a world which wasn't mine. I very soon learned that I wasn't made for the society which half opened its doors to me and is now closing them again. I wasn't born to shine, to cut a swathe, to strut perpetually on the boards. That no doubt is why, if I retain a nostalgia for this fleeting success, my regrets are very amply compensated for.

I will no longer be haunted by thoughts of the performance I must give, the actor's stage fright, the worry of having to prepare topics of conversation, of knowing what one must say in order to appear up to date. I'll no longer feel myself obliged to step up my batteries on entering a salon because the current I normally have at my disposal isn't enough to run me at the speed of my fellow guests. It's good, by and large, no longer to be forced to Play the Game. Restful not to have ceaselessly to find something new to say. Wonderful to sit back in a chair and be myself, without feeling afraid to admit that I've done nothing of what is "done," seen nothing of what is seen and dined in a restaurant which was neither Maxim's nor the Tour d'Argent. To be simply myself, without caring what others are thinking; to remain silent without wondering if the desire to be silent is going to be taken for inadequate powers of conversation, or for stupidity, or for indifference.

I have the impression of being left alone on a beach from which the sea has withdrawn. Invitations have become fewer and fewer. The new friends have disappeared. When Thérèse phones them, they have gone away, are going away, or are about to go away. The horse has been put up for sale. I've sold my shares. Thérèse has kept her little car, but I got rid of mine. This causes me more satisfaction than inconvenience; how delightful it is to be able to walk in the streets of Paris without having your fellow

citizens hurling imprecations after you. Only a few over-
due bills still come in to remind me that there was a time
when I could think myself rich. The children, more and
more absorbed in their own lives, barely notice the change.
As for Thérèse, she's making up for her disappointment
with what was always her forte, housekeeping—and the
new baby, nicknamed Point-Three.

Barnage had no idea how right he was when he tried to
assure me that I was happier in the days when I lived in
obscurity. By concealing me from birth from the sight of
others, heaven had perhaps given me the key to a happiness
I couldn't as yet appreciate. After having been ignored, I
was made too much of. By women in particular. What had
to happen happened: There was, once again, a woman.
Another Miriam. And once again, straddled between life
and the theater, I played one of those scenes the progress
of which I've already described. I found the same words. I
heard the same retorts. I used the same subterfuges. Only
the setting of my escapades had changed; it had extended—
Venice replaced Le Lavandou. But the obstacles remained
the same. If anything, they increased, because my face,
which formerly meant nothing to anyone, now meant a lot
to far too many people.

And now that too is in the past. A day came when I no
longer felt young enough for permanent clandestinity, or
that my nerves were strong enough to spin out threads of
lies one by one and organize the network of accomplices

every time I went away. The fiber of the pensioner had thickened in me. I had succumbed to the vertigo of resignation. I no longer resented growing old: I felt at peace.

With this little house in the country—the only thing left from the contest—I'm beginning to fall in love with a new life, perhaps the true one: not those little social pleasures which demand a great effort of thought for a tiny tickling of one's self-esteem, but that of the birds, flowers, nature. Of course it's not unpleasant, as my old investment adviser intimated, to tread the earth and say to yourself, "This is mine!" But what I enjoy here most of all is the supreme luxury of our age, that most sacred and most violated of possessions: silence. Even though the contest and its glories enabled me to travel in search of distant paradises, everywhere I was pursued by noise. You can put any price on any voyage, but nothing will guarantee that at Tierra del Fuego or on the Galapagos you won't be joined by some of those tourists who never feel at ease unless they're butchering silence within a hundred-yard radius by means of their adorable little scourge of a portable radio. Oh, how sweet it is at sunset on Lake Garda to hear the murmur of "Wash It Bright with Vax Tonight!" and how proud of your era you feel when, as you contemplate the Matterhorn, you're brought back to earth by a commentator in the Pentagon: "This is Jim Jones speaking to you from Washington!"

Lord of a tiny domain, I am master of the waves. And no one can come to shatter my eardrums by force with music or voices which I don't wish to hear. It's a great deal.

252

Miriam . . . our escapades . . . the contest . . . M. Paparakis and the Comte de Rieussec . . . How far away it all seems already! The days fall one after another, shoveled up like ashes over those bygone times when the contest raised me to the level of a star. The moment is close at hand when nobody will remember it at all.

More voracious than the divinities of the Aztecs, the Goddess Topicality demands new heads. Quick to enthrone kings and queens, she is even quicker to knock them off their pedestals. There must be new names for the headlines, new faces for the magazine covers.

In this hotel at St.-Flour where I'm spending the night, my face lies tattered and torn on a pitch-pine table top among the dog-eared magazines in the lounge. That was me, in color. And yet, when I signed the hotel register, neither my name nor my face seemed to mean anything to the manager. I must have lost my coloring. Another little shovelful of earth . . .

More and more each day, I'm once again becoming the old Blot, the Blot whose face failed to catch people's eyes, the Blot who slipped past the gaze of the world. Soon they will have forgotten the very reason which lifted me up for a brief space out of obscurity. Until the moment comes when, fulfilling to the very end the conditions laid down for me by destiny at the start, I'll efface myself forever . . .

Rubbed out.